VICTORY SALVO

VICTORY SALVO

BY

GUN BUSTER

Windrow & Greene

First published 1946 by
Hodder & Stoughton Ltd.

This edition published 1994 by
Windrow & Greene Ltd.
19A Floral Street
London WC2E 9DS

A CIP record for this book is
available from the British Library

ISBN 1 85915 006 3

Printed and bound in Great Britain by
Biddles Ltd, Guildford and King's Lynn

CONTENTS

I—Keren Kate

The four 6-in. howitzers, Mark I, stood parked beneath the spreading elms in the corner of the big field up the Hampshire lane where the Troop was under canvas. They had just arrived, fresh from Ordnance. And they shouted the fact of their virginity aloud. A filthy, forbidding, bluish-grey grease besmeared each gun, grease half-an-inch thick. Grease daubed the exterior of the piece. Grease upon grease choked the barrel. Grease lay plastered over all the working parts and the brass. The elevating arc was simply—grease. By way of a change, the breech was sealed fast with mineral jelly—a brownish poultice instead of a bluish. "Touch-me-not . . ." it all shouted. And none of the crowd of gunners from the Troop's four sub-sections, gloomily surveying their new possessions, felt the slightest desire not to obey.

For over five weeks the Troop had been waiting on the pleasure of Ordnance. At last the high gods condescended. Earlier in the day the Lieutenant-Quartermaster, four sergeants and four limber-gunners from the sub-sections, and a fatigue party had gone forth in Matadors to collect the guns from the railway station, five miles away. The result of their labours was now visible to all. And the gunners eyed it askance. Nothing indicative of their immediate travail escaped them. Not even the thick coat of dust picked up by the guns on their journey, which mingled with the outer layers of grease in a still more repulsive mixture.

"A fine bloody mess for us to clean," was the general verdict. It was announced without any reserve, and even the limber-gunners who, as everyone knows, are by nature men with tender spots in their hearts for guns, had to admit that, at first sight, this howitzer quartette appeared to be entirely unlovable. All were foul to look upon. But one was fouler. Upon her the grease lay even thicker than upon her companions. The inside of her barrel was something to shudder at. Dust covered her like a horrible scurf. She was obscene. . . .

The Sergeant of D sub-section walked round her distastefully.

"What a bastard . . ." he said. "I hope we don't get that one."

His limber-gunner, a dark, quiet man, with a deprecatory voice, united himself in the hope.

Accompanied by their limber-gunners, the four sergeants who were the Numbers One of the sub-sections, went about from gun to gun, passing each under a searching examination preparatory to the moment of selection. To the uninitiated one 6-in. howitzer smothered in grease is as good as another. Not so to a Number One. And even less so to a limber-gunner, upon whom rests the responsibility for the complete maintenance of both gun and stores. Howitzers have their idiosyncracies, like human beings. And it is the limber-gunner, with knowledge fortified by affection who, above all other men in the battery, not excluding the Major, is best equipped to weigh in the balance the respective merits of one gun against another, be the virgin grease never so thick. Everything tells him something—the way the gun behaves on quick release, the way the loading tray fits into the slides, the action of the traversing wheels, even the way the handspikes fit into the sockets on the trail. Such are some of the factors making one gun a different being from another.

The limber-gunner of sub-section D overlooked nothing. His attention dwelt just as weightily upon such things as the hatchet straps, the straps for the loading tray, the leather-covering over the brakes, as it did on the degree of ease with which the trail worked. At the close of the examination he and the Sergeant exchanged views. It was agreed that, all things considered, there wasn't much in it so far as the actual guns were concerned.

"In that case we'll go for the one that's easiest to clean," said the Sergeant. "At least, we know what we don't want," he added with a significant nod towards the double-greased pariah at the far end of the line.

Surrounded by their adherents the four Numbers One gathered together and tossed up their coins. First pick fell to C sub-section, and second to A. This left to be disposed of only the unmentionable and her neighbour, a gun that, by comparison, looked as if it merely wanted a bucket of hot water thrown over it to become quite presentable.

"Don't make any mistake next time, sarge," implored sub-section D, afflicted with the sudden vision of themselves spending uncountable hours at the end of a piassaba brush.

The coin spun in the air. Their Sergeant called: "Heads." It was Tails. . . .

A great groan ascended from the victims. It was swamped by ironic cheers from the other three sub-sections. None of them was at all sorry that misfortune had fallen where it had. D sub-section was the crack sub-section of the Battery. And they were at pains to let everyone know it. D sub-section regarded all the prizes in Battery competitions for the best-kept gun as theirs in advance by divine right. It was as good as a year's combined consolation prize to their rivals to think of all the grease that awaited sub-section D.

The defeated Sergeant recovered his shaken dignity.

"It's all yours," he said abruptly to the limber-gunner. "Do what you like with it."

Then he hurried off to the Sergeants' Mess to escape further unflattering comment on his powers of guessing the right side of a spinning coin.

The limber-gunner, attended by a handful of disconsolates, walked up to his new charge in quite a friendly way.

"It's the best gun of the lot," he affirmed, with quiet conviction.

Already, like a fond mother, he was prepared to maintain the worth of his own against all challengers.

Next morning, after parade, a procession of unenthusiastic gunners clad in brown overalls, and armed with buckets of hot water, rags, sticks, and other implements for the administration of cleanliness to virgin howitzers, made their reluctant way across the field to the corner under the elms. The Limber-gunner of sub-section D already awaited his staff of assistants, with the breech of the howitzer open, and the stores-box lifted off the trail. Hence followed many a long, hot, perspiring hour during which time the gunners dug the grease off the gun in chunks, and wiped it off in layers, and varied the pastime by swilling-out the barrel with interminable buckets of hot water, until the continual elevating and depressing of the gun threatened to give them vertigo. Morning yielded to afternoon, and still they washed and scrubbed and scraped. Once or twice the Sergeant strolled over to inspect progress, and prescribed further scrubbing here, and scraping there. The grease-bedaubed gunners, regarding him (unfairly) as the sole author of their misfortunes, grew gloomier than ever. Only the Limber-gunner, toiling like a slave himself, preserved throughout an air of quiet contentment, even of enthusiasm, which sometimes encouraged his fellow-labourers, and sometimes gave them a pain.

The afternoon wore away. At last the Limber-gunner, taking a squint down the bore, noticed that it was beginning to shine. True, it was a long way from the mirror-like surface which was his ultimate goal. Nevertheless his heart gladdened. The end was in sight. A film of oil was squirted down. A rag was wrapped round the piassaba brush. And five sweating gunners entered upon a new purgatory. When they emerged from it, exhausted, you could have shaved yourself with a month-old safety-razor in front of their achievement.

Needless to say, the three other sub-sections were finished long before. Some of the men strolled up to enjoy the spectacle of D sub-section's labours. The weary gunners found the crackle of witticisms hard to bear.

The limber-gunner said nothing and looked nothing. In his usual quiet, reserved way he went on with his job as though completely oblivious of a deriding audience. And it was in the same quiet casual manner that, in due course, he produced a tin of metal polish.

At sight of this the fire of sarcasm died down. The onlookers watched subsequent operations in an intense silence. They saw the breech-carrier polished till it shone like the sun. And likewise all the other brass parts, the lever-breech mechanism, bits of the sight brackets, elevating and traversing wheels, the hubs on the wheels. . . .

They could contain themselves no longer. To-morrow was Saturday. In the morning was C.O.'s inspection. And they knew it.

"What are you polishing all that for?" they protested indignantly. "Now we shall be expected to do it."

The faintest crease of a grin appeared at the corners of the Limber-gunner's mouth. Being a quiet, reserved man he was perfectly satisfied with his revenge.

The sun began to drop. The day's great work was done. Having given the brake handle a last, and quite superfluous rub, the Limber-gunner and his valiant nine stood back to appreciate the results of their labours. Weary and grease-besmeared as they were, they had to admit that they had something to show for their pains. The howitzer stood revealed spotless and workman-like, in all her squat, bull-dog beauty. She did them credit. And under the influence of this flattery their feelings softened towards her.

"What are we going to christen her?" remarked the Sergeant.

There are Troops whose commanders jealously reserve to themselves the right to christen their guns. A man interested in racing, say, will want his guns named after past winners of the Derby. Another, with classical leanings, will have them baptized "Plato," "Socrates," "Homer" etc. (But these are not many). Other T.C.'s don't care a damn one way or the other. The 6-in. howitzer Troop Commander was one of these. To the deputation of sergeants paying him the compliment of enquiring what names he would like bestowed on the four new arrivals, he had made reply; "Call them anything you fancy. So long as it is respectable."

Sub-sections A, B, and C had already named their guns "Iron Duke," "Daisy" and "Crippen" respectively. But whether it was that D sub-section were so exhausted by their extended labours that their imagination could not soar to baptismal pitch, or whether the stultifying grease had entered their souls, or whether the grudge they bore against the gun at first sight was still operative, the fact remains that they were not in the mood for evolving pet names. After one or two half-hearted attempts, there were no further suggestions.

" We'll let her be for the present," decided the Sergeant. " The old bastard. . . ."

" You've said it, sarge," exclaimed the crew, almost as one man. " The old bastard . . . That's her."

And Old Bastard it was.

Experts in the art of nomenclature will not fail to note that the addition of the adjective denoted a subtle change of attitude from the evening before when the Sergeant had found that the bald noun fully sufficed to express his sentiments.

The adjective marked a decided, though slight, advance in friendship.

Next morning the Sergeant and the Limber-gunner stood by their gun while the Major, attended by the Battery Captain, the Troop Commander, and the Lieutenant-Quartermaster, made his inspection. They had every reason to await the result with confidence. In the bright sunshine the howitzer looked a picture of loving care and attention. As indeed it was. For the Limber-gunner had not ceased fondling it till nine o'clock the previous evening. And he had made a point of going out before breakfast that morning to test for " air and oil."

Being at the end of the line D sub-section's gun was the last visited by the Major. He went through the usual bag of tricks, trying the elevating arc and the traversing wheel, and squinting down the bore.

" Well done, Sergeant . . ." was the verdict. And to the Limber-gunner ; " Excellent work. Keep it up . . ."

Just as he was departing the Major asked ; " And what have you called *your* gun ? "

The Sergeant hesitated. Remembering the Troop Commander's injunction, and was not quite sure whether " bastard " was regarded as a respectable word in the Officers' Mess, he decided to be on the safe side.

" Haven't christened her yet, sir " he said, without a blink.

The inspection party passed on. Later in the morning word filtered through to the sub-section from the Troop-Commander that the Major had expressed himself in terms of the highest satisfaction at the condition of their gun. Naturally they assumed this to mean that he hadn't been so much impressed by "Iron Duke," "Daisy," and "Crippen."

"One up to the Old Bastard," they cried, generously giving the gun all the credit.

* * *

Three days later the regiment received orders to proceed overseas, and the guns had to be all greased-up again.

II

Abyssinia was their destination. The regiment disembarked at Port Said and proceeded some distance southwards to Mena Camp. Here, still feeling slightly self-conscious in their khaki topees, D sub-section settled down with its fellows to await the arrival of their guns, which were also coming by way of Port Said. They waited nearly a month, oscillating between daily rumours that the guns had been landed or that they had been torpedoed on the voyage. Although gunners separated from their guns for any length of time are inclined to feel they have lost something of themselves D sub-section, generally speaking, supported the delay with equanimity. The exception was the Limber-gunner who, being a man only happy in the company of mechanism, and also having already developed quite an affection for the Old Bastard, displayed an ever-present concern as to its fate, and haunted the Battery Office for latest news. The remainder of the crew always knew the nature of the current rumour of the day without being told. If the guns were reported landed the Limber-gunner returned from the Office quiet and reserved. If they were reported sunk, he returned more quiet and more reserved.

At last all doubts were stilled. The guns arrived. And the Limber-gunner settled down to the congenial task of ungreasing the Old Bastard for a second time. But on this occasion it was much easier work. The gunners had provided for that. Knowing full well that what they put on they would have to take off, they had been far less lavish with the grease than Ordnance.

At Cairo the guns were mounted on flat railway trucks and they began their long journey south into the desert with the muddy sluggish Nile alongside as their eternal companion. So they reached Shellal, just below Aswan, a native village squatting among low rocks and sand by the side of the Nile, and bearing welcome signs of the march of civilisation in the shape of a Military Transit Camp and, more important to D sub-section, a N.A.F.F.I. where warm beer could be obtained.

At Shellal the railway finished with them. Their further progress was to be by paddle-steamer of the old Mississippi show-boat style, flat-bottomed, big-hipped with paddle-wheels, and sprouting a long narrow chimney-pot of a funnel. Shallow-draught barges were drawn alongside the low bank to receive the guns and their transport.

Having deposited their kit-bags in the steamer the gun crews fortified by the N.A.F.F.I., began the arduous task of embarking their howitzers under a broiling afternoon sun and in an atmosphere humid and enervating from the exhalations of the wide, palm-fringed Nile. These were not the ideal conditions for man-handling 6-in. howitzers. Each gun-crew attended to its own weapon, the sergeant directing operations, with the Troop Commander keeping an eye upon the whole. Four men naked to the waist, held up the trail of the howitzer with handspikes and the gun was gradually coaxed up a ramp of planks leading from the flat shore to the barge. Other gun numbers, pulling at drag-ropes from the barge, rendered assistance at essential moments.

It was slow, ticklish work. And the humid heat rendered it more ticklish. The ramp was not very wide, and as 6-in. howitzers under the process of man-handling often develop mulish tendencies to go in every direction but the one required, much adroitness as well as muscular power, had to be employed to guide the gun into the barge instead of into the Nile.

"Together . . . Heave . . ."

"Trail right . . . Heave."

"Trail left . . . Heave."

So it went on hour after hour, under the merciless sun, before an appreciative audience on the bank, consisting of whole families of natives, and gunners who had either finished their own job, or whose time had not yet come.

Four guns were allotted to each barge. When it came to D sub-section's turn, being the last of the Troop, they found themselves confronted by a pretty problem. The lorries and guns of the other three sub-sections almost monopolised the whole space of the barge. There was just room for the Old Bastard to creep in with its trail tucked between the wheels of the other guns. This meant that the gun must slip into final position, like a bolt into a slot, direct from the top of the ramp. There was no space on the barge itself for manœuvring.

For something approaching an hour the Sergeant of D sub-section brought to bear upon his problem the complete resources of that part of the drill-book devoted to the manipulation of 6-in. howitzers. He also invoked the aid of less orthodox methods. Both alike failed to meet the emergency. The gun obstinately refused to fit into its narrow bed. On many occasions they seemed to be heading for success. But at the last moment a few inches cheated them. And this was just one of those cases where a miss is as good as a mile.

"Trail left . . . Heave. . . ."

The harassed Sergeant's voice grew dry and hoarse from the constant reiteration of orders. As if to exert his personal influence with the gun, the Limber-gunner seized one of the drag-ropes himself and began tugging his heart out. The steaming afternoon boiled over. A fresh team relieved the dripping four at the handspikes, and in no length of time the sweat was pouring in appreciable tributaries to the Nile itself, off their naked torsos also. Tempers began to shorten and fray. The Troop Commander manifested distinct signs of impatience. On the bank of the river the spectators had long since realised they were beholding no mere exercise in repository but yet one more act in the everlasting drama of Man versus Destiny. Their rapt interest would have done credit to an Athenian audience having its passions purged by Æschylus in the theatre of Dionysus.

"Heave . . ." roared the Sergeant for the thousand-and-fiftieth time.

The gun began to lumber from the top of the ramp on to the barge. Hopes ran high. It was their most propitious attempt of the afternoon.

" Mind you don't fall in . . ." the Sergeant warned the handspike numbers who were perilously near the edge of the ramp.

" Trail left . . ."

So anxious was the Sergeant not to miss this golden opportunity that he could not wait for his order to be obeyed. He stepped off the barge on to the ramp to lend a hand himself, and pulled at the trail where the handspike fitted into the eye.

" Together . . . Heave. . . ."

The drag-ropes responded. So did the trail. So did the Sergeant. He disappeared off the ramp with a resounding splash. Old Nile received him upon her flat, shallow bosom. A filthy mixture of oily water and black mud enveloped him.

The Sergeant's sojourn in the alluvial regions was brief but rich in power to transform. When next he appeared to the world of mortals it was as a spluttering caricature of some broken-down, pantomime Neptune. From head downwards he was festooned with green weeds and green slime. It hung over his face from the brim of his topee and draped his sodden shirt with evil, clinging pendants more than a foot long. Where he wasn't a foul green he was a foul black.

For a moment or two, invisible below the waist, he stood rooted in the river while he recovered his bearings. Then, having brushed clear his eyes and spat out a couple of mouthfuls of vile Nile, he addressed the Universe on his woes. It was a magnificent effort. The Sergeant never repeated himself once. And his best epithets were reserved for the howitzer which had been the cause of his misfortune. He ransacked the confines of a vast and erudite vocabulary to find terms in which to describe her, addressing her personally where she stood with her trail hanging over the side of the barge. The gunners on the ramp had jammed on the brake. So they were free to join in the loud, long laugh that the Sergeant's astonishing metamorphosis had let loose.

Cursing and spluttering the Sergeant waded ashore. The crowd of grinning gunners and natives on the bank hastened to make way for him, as the crowd always will pay deference to the obviously mighty. And mighty the Sergeant was. A mighty stench. He had brought up from the river-bed odours undisturbed since the days of Pharaoh, and by now astoundingly rank. His arc of fire was deadly within a radius of thirty yards. He was unapproachable.

Nevertheless he made to mount the ramp in order to resume his labours. The occupants shrank back before his approach. The Troop Commander, whose nose was peculiarly sensitive to smells, hastily intervened.

" I think you've done your share for the time being, Sergeant," he said diplomatically. " Better go and get a change of kit."

The Sergeant disappeared on to the paddle-steamer. A sergeant from another sub-section was called upon to wrestle with the problem. As often happens luck favoured the new comer. At the first attempt the Old Bastard did exactly what was required of her and a minute or two later she was tucked neatly in with the other guns on the barge.

Late that evening when they were proceeding up-river towards Wadi Halfa the Limber-gunner, who had preserved a very reserved and thoughtful demeanour ever since the incident on the ramp, unburdened himself to the bombardier.

" I can understand sarge's feelings at the moment," he said mildly. " I agree he was suffering great provocation. But I don't think he ought to have let himself go as he did against the gun. The gun wasn't to blame.

" Guns, I know, have their peculiar ways, like human beings, and can be very exasperating at times," he continued, speaking in the saddened tone of a man defending one of his friends against an unfair attack by another. " But in this case the gun couldn't have done anything else. It simply obeyed the order. I didn't like to hear sarge blackguarding it for no fault of its own."

The bombardier listened with mixed respect and amusement.

" Limber, you're a marvel . . ." he said.

III

Death Valley . . .

So the gunners called it. And so it might lay claim to be called, independent of the deadly thunder of artillery that rolled up and down it, day after day. A grim, ungodly spot . . . Naked except for a parched scrub, and scored with dried-up watercourses, the valley was heavily frowned upon by a harsh and forbidding ridge of gloomy rock rising sheer from the plain. Iron-cliff piled upon iron-cliff, serrated with knife-edges, and topped at last by monstrous peaks of steep black rock which projected into the sultry sky at a height of nearly three-thousand feet, like merciless fangs from a jagged jawbone. Fit furniture for a Dantesque inferno. . . .

The Troop of 6-in. howitzers to which the Old Bastard belonged now formed part of the medium artillery of the 4th Indian Division which was immersed, and had been so for weeks, in the attempt to storm the Italian mountain citadel of Keren. Twice the Indian infantry had, with incredible determination, managed to scale the rocky bastions barring the road to the fortress. Twice they had been pushed off after a desperate and bloody struggle. For the time being the battle had died down into a protracted series of artillery duels.

For eight days the Troop had been in action in sand-bagged gun-pits in a shallow wadi, with the road to Keren running through the valley before them. They had a splendid view of the ferocious scenery on the other side. And the enemy, as he had already indicated, had a pretty good view of them. Cover was so scanty that the gun-pits were little more than holes scooped in the desert. It was impossible to hope to escape observation from the towering peaks opposite. And especially did the Troop feel the pressing attentions of the one known as Brig's Peak, the black plateau of which was still in Italian hands.

The Old Bastard had the dubious advantage of being dug in under a grey thorn tree, seared with the intolerable heat, and armed with fearsome thorns three-inches long. Thirty yards behind was the Command Post, a slit trench, where the Gun Position Officer crouched with his artillery board and his assistant, a lance-sergeant.

It was three o'clock in the afternoon, an afternoon of sapping, sultry heat. The thermometer registered 130 degrees. What it was in the shade hardly mattered because there never was any shade except first thing in the morning and last thing at night. There had been a lull in the firing, and under the influence of a dinner of bully-beef stew the men lay dozing in the gun-pits, their faces covered with veils cut from mosquito nets to keep off the hordes of stinging flies.

" Take Post . . ." suddenly shouted the G.P.O. from the Command Post. The Troop Commander who was up at the O.P. had just sent down a target.

The veiled gun-screws stood-to. But before any further orders came from the Gun Position Officer, a shell burst just behind them and another just in front. More followed in quick succession. They had been discovered by an Italian pack-battery perched high on Brig's Peak. There was nothing for it but to close down for the time being.

" Take cover . . ." roared the G.P.O. through his megaphone.

With the shells bursting all round them the gunners scrambled out of the pits and dived into the slit trenches dug in an arc behind the guns. It appeared almost as if the Italian gunners had singled out the Old Bastard for their prime attentions. Huddled in their trenches, only four yards behind the gun-pit, D sub-section found themselves at the core of the bombardment. One deafening explosion succeeded another. The earth went up in continual fountains of sand and dust and stones, that rained down heavily upon them.

The blistering air filled with cordite fumes, half-choking them. A couple of shells hit the charges stacked just outside the gun-pit, and they went up with a hoarse whoof and a tremendous flash. The camouflage net was in flames. After five minutes of this pulverisation came a particularly violent crack.

" That's dead in the gun-pit, I bet," guessed the bombardier in the trench behind. " I reckon I've laid the Old Bastard for the last time."

He suddenly grabbed at the Limber-gunner who was about to thrust his head over the top.

"Keep down, you blasted fool," he shouted. "Here comes another."

"I was only anxious to see whether anything had happened to the gun," said the Limber-gunner, mildly. "I hope she's all right."

Immediately afterwards a shell dropped on top of the adjacent trench wherein the Sergeant was sheltering with four gunners. There was a roar, a shower of falling debris, and then silence.

Seeing what had happened, the Gun Position Officer ran towards the spot shouting : "Are you all right ? . . ."

While he waited for a reply two of the occupants of the ill-fated trench crawled out from the ruins. They were the Sergeant and one of the gunners. They were almost unrecognisable, their faces and shirts blackened with cordite soot. The other two gunners had been blown to pieces. A stone had smashed the ankle of the surviving gunner. Between them, the G.P.O. and the Sergeant conveyed him to the shelter of the Command Post.

The shelling lasted twenty-minutes, and when it was over D sub-section felt they had had their share. They crawled back to the gun-pit to inspect the damage there. The bombardier had been both right and wrong. A shell had dropped in the gun-pit. It had exploded right underneath the trail of the gun. But, miraculously, the Old Bastard had survived. The only signs of her ordeal were two holes in the trail and a few marks on the exterior of the piece where it had been chipped by shrapnel. Even the dial sight was uninjured. The Limber-gunner provided a study in solicitude. Quietly, like a doctor examining a patient, he went all over the gun, inch by inch, to reassure himself that she had received no secret wounds. And having made sure he patted her approvingly on the muzzle.

Meantime, D sub-section prepared to bury its dead. The remains of the two gunners were collected and wrapped in blankets. But not all of them. Skewered on the three-inch spikes of the thorn tree over the gun-pit were odd rags of flesh and clothing. Nobody fancied the job of detaching them, so they were left to shrivel and bleach in the sun. A grave was dug in front of the gun-pit, in full view of Brig's Peak, and edged round with white stones. The Battery carpenter constructed a very nice cross from a milk-case. The blankets were lowered into the grave. The Troop Commander, back from the O.P., said a few appropriate words. So did the Sergeant. But not till the hole had been filled-up.

"We'll give 'em an ice-cream for that," he said.

From the dead they turned their attention to the living.

"I think it's time we christened our gun," said the Limber-gunner.

"Hasn't she got a name already ?" the Sergeant replied.

"That was only temporary," said the Limber-gunner, who, in his heart of hearts, had always regarded the name as derogatory to his charge, and made a point of never using it himself. "I think it's time we gave her a name she can be proud of," he continued. "After all, she deserves it. Look at the way she stood up to all that shelling. She's got battle-scars to show."

"I don't mind," said the Sergeant. "What do you suggest ?"

"I thought 'Keren' would be suitable, in the circumstances."

"Keren . . . That's only half a name. Keren what . . ?"

The answer came from one of the gunners, inspired by a soldier's joint fondness for the feminine and the alliterative in the matter of nick-names.

"Kate . . ."

"That's it . . . 'Keren Kate'," agreed the Sergeant.

There were no objections. Everyone considered it to be an ideal name. The Limber-gunner wasted no time. He went off at once and returned shortly with a tin of white paint and painted K.K. in large letters on the carriage underneath the muzzle of the gun.

Thus, after many, many days, in the iron-ribbed confines of Death Valley, did the Old Bastard snap the last link binding her to her greasy past.

Next morning the G.P.O. appeared in the gun-pit.

"Sergeant, how much switch can you manage east and west of zero line ?" he inquired. "Get the gun-pit clear for a big switch, if necessary. We're going to do an aeroplane shoot."

"On that pack-battery that gave me a black face yesterday, I hope, sir," said the Sergeant, fervently.

The G.P.O. nodded his agreement with this sentiment.

"Maybe it is," he replied, non-committally. "The shoot will last for ten minutes. And the instant it is finished take cover. Don't forget."

The news that they were going to have their revenge for the white-stoned grave in front of the gun-pit, and the horrible trimmings on the thorn tree, enlivened the spirits of the sub-section to a degree beyond the power of a particularly hot and sultry morning to suppress. When, at twelve o'clock, the Hurricane that was to conduct the shoot commenced operations by circling low over the gun positions D sub-section gave it a hearty cheer. In the interval the Limber-gunner had been active getting Keren Kate into first-rate trim for her première. For so he regarded it. He was quite fussy and anxious that the gun's debut under her new name should be a marked success. And, in lesser measure, the whole sub-section felt likewise. They felt that their gun had a name to live up to. And they had never quite felt like that before. They stood-to in the mood of confident backers round their champion just before he enters the ring.

The Hurricane soared aloft. The Gun Position Officer began to shout the orders.

"Fresh target . . . Aeroplane shoot . . . H.E. 119 . . . Charge 3 . . ." He gave them the zero line, angle of sight and range. "Fire by order . . . One round salvo . . ."

The two loading numbers rammed the shell home into Keren Kate's glistening breech with a hearty thrust. With his usual quiet, unhurried motion, the Limber-gunner whose job is was to fire the gun, fixed the lanyard on to the extension wire of the lock, stepped a yard aside from the gun, and waited. The Sergeant stood beside the gun, holding the rammer vertically with his hand at the top, a sign to the Gun Position Officer that Keren Kate was now at his disposal. In the other three pits the sergeants also planted their hands at the top of the rammers as their preparations were complete.

"Down D . . . Down C . . . Down A . . . Down B . . ." shouted the G.P.O. in turn.

When each sergeant had dropped his hand from his rammer, the G.P.O. knew that all was ready for the salvo.

"Fire! . . ."

The four guns roared almost as one, and the salvo burst out of sight in the rocky recesses of Brig's Peak.

Back came a correction from the Hurricane, which was passed to the guns. The layers put it on. The trails were traversed, the guns loaded, and laid afresh.

"Fire! . ."

This time, the pilot of the Hurricane, a South African, was so overcome by the result that the strict routine of his job failed to curb his pardonable ebullience. Instead of sending back: "On target . . ." and the appropriate number of rounds gunfire, the message that, in an excited voice, reached the G.P.O. through his ear-phones was:

"Whoopee, boys . . . Oh, whoopee! . . . Medium shells falling right in the middle of the bastards . . ."

But it wasn't of much consequence. The G.P.O. grabbed his megaphone and roared:

"Ten rounds gunfire . . . Sweep and search . . ."

As fast as the guns could be re-loaded the shells went screaming across the valley. In four minutes it was over.

"Take cover! . . ." shouted the G.P.O.

And the gunners tumbled out of the four gun-pits without further inducement. This time their goal was not the slit trenches but the far side of a low sand-ridge, a hundred yards away. Mindful of their experience of the previous afternoon they went for it like greyhounds out of the trap, all except the sergeants, who had a dignity to preserve. It was a very creditable hundred yards sprint, considering such handicaps as heat and rough going. But even then they only got to their cover in the nick of time. A rain of shells descended on the area. The thunder rolled up and down Death Valley, echoing from peak to peak without a break, so that it was easy to imagine that the entire complement of enemy artillery in Abyssinia had suddenly been let loose. It lasted for five minutes. And did nothing.

Later, at tea-time, when the four sub-sections lined-up with their mugs before the dixie on the stove under the gun-tarpaulin, which was the Troop cookhouse, a lively argument started. It began modestly enough, with D sub-section's assertion that Keren Kate had been the fastest in getting off its rounds during the aeroplane shoot. This the other sub-sections refused to allow. They would go no further than the admission that D sub-section had been fastest in running for cover. Hence, with D sub-section in one of its cockiest moods, the argument developed till it was alleged, not without grounds, that the sub-section was claiming the entire credit for the success of the shoot.

"You couldn't see where your shells were bursting," protested their aggrieved rivals, heatedly.

"We *know* where they were," D sub-section retorted with vigour.

"Where ?"

"On the I-ti's."

"Why ?"

The demand was made very aggressively, but D sub-section were not in the slightest perturbed. They produced their proofs. These were brief and cogent. And like oil to flames.

"Why ? . . . Because we've got the best Number One. And the best limber. And the best layer. And the best loading-numbers. And the best gun. . . ."

Quite an uproar drowned this final assertion. D sub-section rallied to the defence of Keren Kate as one man. It surprised themselves to discover how much, unconsciously, they had come to admire her. They stood up for her with a real warmth of affection, headed, of course, by the Limber-gunner.

The argument threatened to last out the campaign. It was interrupted from an unexpected quarter. Three of the Troop drivers round the dixie announced that they had had enough. They strenuously voiced their complete and utter weariness at having to listen every meal-time to nothing but everlasting rival boosts of guns, guns, guns. . . .

"And never a bloody word about the lorries. . . ."

Whereupon the gunners of the four sub-sections united to instruct the drivers as to the relative stations of 6-in. howitzers and lorries in the Ordained Scheme of Things.

The storm died away in the tea-cup.

IV

Still Death Valley . . . But the howitzer Troop were now in new positions higher up. The hard nut of Keren was still to crack. And Keren Kate was still pounding away for all she was worth. By this time she had fired thousands of rounds. A couple of thousand would have been a creditable figure, but Keren Kate's record far exceeded that. The whole of D sub-section was unreservedly proud of the number of rounds she had fired and of the accuracy with which she had fired them. Her arduous labours did not seem to have told upon her at all. She could be relied upon, as much as ever, to drop her shells just where they were wanted. It was a joy to the Troop Commander, up at the O.P., to see the unfaltering way in which she responded to his corrections. And, likewise, it was a joy to the gun-crew to fire her.

In other aspects, however, Keren Kate had undergone conspicuous changes. There was not much outward resemblance now between her and the well-groomed, spotless howitzer that had given the Sergeant his taste of Old Nile. She looked all over the war-stained veteran that she was. Her glossiness had vanished. She was just rough and uncouth. Her green, brown and black camouflage was dirty and worn, and clothed her like a filthy skin. Shrapnel chips scarred the exterior of the piece and also the carriage. The trail was caked with hard dust. The wood by the brackets where the loaders jammed their feet when ramming home the shells, was no longer hard and smooth and clean, but splintered, black, and oily. When you looked down the muzzle, instead of the beautiful silvery finish of the bore, it was a well-coppered hue that met the eye, a legacy from the copper driving-bands of the thousands of 100-pound shells that had passed that way. Sometimes the Limber-gunner grew quite melancholy when he contrasted her present neglected appearance with the spruce gun that had won commendation on C.O.'s inspection in days gone by. But there was nothing he could do about it. Lack of time and lack of facilities were against him. Instead of copious supplies of oily rags and hot water Keren Kate was often very lucky now if she got a quick once-over with a dry brush. In one respect, however, the Limber-gunner did preserve all the old standards. The breech was as shining and spotless as ever. The slightest opportunity sufficed for him to begin stripping and cleaning it. Never was he so happy as when engaged on this task. He treasured in his possession like a priceless jewel an almost empty tin of metal polish. No one else was allowed to touch it. The contents were dedicated to the breech and to the breech alone. And a shadow fell on the Limber-gunner whenever he thought of the near approach of the day when the bottom of the exhausted tin would stare him in the face. The result of all this was that if you had gone over the mushroom head of the breech, or the breech-block, with a microscope you would not have been able to detect the slightest sign of cordite burns.

It was towards the close of a particularly grilling day, during which hardly a breath of air had stirred the leaden atmosphere of Death Valley. By way of an evening "hate" the four guns of the Troop were sending over single rounds in turn, at stated intervals. It came to Keren Kate's turn to fire. The Limber-gunner tugged at his lanyard.

The sequel was not quite as expected. After the explosion of the charge, and as the shell left the muzzle, there sounded a pronounced and most unusual "whoof." The Limber-gunner looked over the gun to the Sergeant with a pained surprise. And the Sergeant looked back in surprise without the pain.

"That's a nasty cough," he said. "What's the matter with the old girl?"

The Limber-gunner, highly concerned, opened the breech, and thrust his head forward to see. He was rewarded with a full blast of cordite fumes in his face.

"Her breath stinks," he announced, simply. He might have been talking about some human being who was out of sorts.

The Sergeant burst into a laugh. "P'raps she has got a sore throat," he suggested.

But his sarcasm was quite lost on the Limber-gunner. Like a doctor examining a patient he said:

" I think I'd better take a swab."

He wrapped a cloth round the piassaba brush and gave it a push down the bore. It came out with all the cordite soot on it. The Limber-gunner remained puzzled.

" Give her something to grease her throat with," said the Sergeant.

The Limber-gunner squirted some oil down the muzzle, and once more administered the piassaba brush.

Next time Keren Kate fired she whoofed as loudly as ever.

The Limber-gunner's expression would have done credit to a mother alarmed by the sudden development of feverish symptoms in an only child.

" When we have done firing I'll have to give her a thorough examination," he said, gravely.

" I know what's wrong with her," retorted the Sergeant. " She's suffering from old age. Notice how she recoils ? All jerks. She's had her day. Time she was sent to the scrap-heap. She's finished."

This ungenerous and summary verdict upon his charge fired even the mild disposition of the Limber-gunner into protest.

" No, sarge," he declared, stoutly. " She isn't finished by a long way yet. That gun's a marvel. You'll never see another like her. Old age ? . . . Why, she's as good now as the day she came out of Ordnance. There's nothing tired about Keren Kate."

" All right, all right," replied the Sergeant. " But what are you going to do about her ? "

In the event, Keren Kate was shown to have vindicated completely the Limber-gunner's good opinion of her. Her complaint was diagnosed as gravity tank trouble, not old age. Owing to the continual firing the nuts had worked loose and the tank caught on the trunnions and got knocked off. The artificer re-affixed it.

The Sergeant summoned a driver and lorry, put a winch through the barrel of the gun, and pulled the piece back with the winch-gear.

" Let go . . ." he shouted.

The brake was taken off and the gun began to slide back. Fast, at first, till the last six inches. Then slow, just as a well-conditioned gun should slide, pushing flush up to the stops on the end of the buffer case.

The cure was complete. Keren Kate coughed no more.

V

Keren had fallen . . . Keren Kate fired the last barrage right the way through, thus putting the seal upon her endeavours of eight solid weeks, during which time she had been firing incessantly, day and night. And now it was good-bye to Death Valley, to Brig's Peak, and to the rest of the infernal scenery. She was to continue her career in a new setting. Orders came for the Battery to proceed northwards to the Libyan desert where, fifteen hundred miles from Keren, a new offensive was being mounted against Rommel and his Afrika Korps. Medium artillery was wanted to join in the push for the relief of the British garrison in Tobruk. And Keren Kate answered to the call.

In due course she found herself at Sidi Annish, twelve miles east of Mersa Matruh, where she was vouchsafed a fortnight's breathing-space before joining in the battle. Here she underwent a transformation. She arrived in the camp, unkempt, scarred, and travel-stained. And though D sub-section were by no means ashamed to appear among new company with their Abyssinian veteran in all its honourable grime and with the two holes in the trail, and the shrapnel chips on the piece, they felt it was high time she returned to the old standards. So, with days at their disposal, the Limber-gunner and his team got busy with their oily rags, and buckets of salt water, and piassaba brush. Nor, on this occasion, were there any reproaches, although she made them sweat. They were proud of the old girl, and couldn't do too much to show it. At last, fitted with a new gravity tank, she emerged from her toilette spick and span, looking quite smart in her desert camouflage, stone-colour with, here and there, a dab of green. The Limber-gunner's final job was to re-paint her name on the carriage, this time in slightly larger letters.

Zero hour . . . They went through the wire in support of the New Zealand infantry who were attacking Fort

Capuzzo. They dug-in, with the three other sub-sections of the howitzer Troop in a semi-circle on the flat desert just behind a low sand ridge. Fort Capuzzo was not more than two thousand yards away. They could easily distinguish the tops of some of the white buildings, and could hear their shells burst and see the earth flung up into the air by the explosions. It was something they could enjoy after their experiences in Death Valley, hammering away week after week at iron-bound peaks which seemed to laugh to scorn their puny efforts.

For three days they remained in these positions, shelling infantry and tank concentrations in Fort Capuzzo, and rather surprised that they had not drawn upon themselves attention from the German bombers. But in their sky up till now the enemy planes had been very few and far between. The R.A.F. were taking too much care of them. To begin with, the howitzers had nothing more to put up with than some counter-shelling from 105 mm. and 155 mm. guns whose shells arrived on top of them with the swish and the explosion almost simultaneous. Later, the Germans, restive under the damage the medium artillery was causing, tried to draw the howitzers towards them by means of a box barrage. For a while Keren Kate and her companions found themselves in a tight corner. But they managed to get out all right.

What bothered the gunners was not so much box barrages as the shortage of rations. The battle had already developed into a fluid, see-saw struggle, with rival tank formations careering over the desert and cropping up in most unexpected places at the most unexpected times. Under these conditions it was difficult to maintain any regularity in the delivery of supplies. Food became very scarce. And water scarcer. Under the brazen sky, sweating and parched, the gunners traversed and loaded and fired, praying for a sight of the water-cart. It was already two days overdue. And no one could forecast when it would arrive. D sub-section's supply was down to half-a-cup of water per man. All the bottles and cans were empty. In these circumstances tea was only something to be dreamed of. The only thing they had in plenty was jam. But no one fancied trying to quench a desert thirst upon that! They preferred to suck pebbles. Rarely five minutes went by without some gunner passing the grim jest to another:

"Mayya (water) for the love of Allah! . . ."

It was getting on for tea-time or, rather, what would have been tea-time under happier auspices. The afternoon had been exceptionally hot and trying, with the flies of the Libyan desert exhibiting much pains to prove to the newcomers that the Abyssinian variety had nothing to teach them. Added to the heat and the thirst, their maddening stings turned the gunners' existence into a torment.

Keren Kate and her fellow howitzers of the Troop were in the final stages of a shoot that had lasted the major part of the afternoon. It was in fact, likely to prove their last shoot in those positions. Enemy tanks were reported coming down from the direction of Bardia in an attempt to cut them off. The rumour had been passed on to the Troop from another battery. Nothing official was known: but it seemed very feasible. So the vehicles had been brought up in readiness, and were now dispersed behind the guns, two hundred yards away, awaiting the order from the Troop Commander to move off.

"I hope to God we move somewhere where the water-wagon will find us," said the Sergeant to the bombardier, in a pause while they were awaiting a new correction from the Gun Position Officer. "What wouldn't I give for a cup of tea, now . . . Curse these flies! . . . They're as thirsty as I am . . ."

"If I weren't so thirsty, I'd be hungry," the bombardier replied.

"I'm both," exclaimed the Sergeant, savagely.

"Well, you can't drink sausages," said the bombardier cheerfully.

On a Primus stove some way behind the gun-pit they could see their tea in preparation. Their driver had just begun to fry some sausages in a frying-pan made from a petrol tin. They had run so short of rations that they had been forced to "borrow" the sausages from another gunner regiment. They had enough for one-and-a-half per man, and the driver had strict orders not to shrink them. The entire gun crew were looking forward to this luxury.

And if there had only been the prospect of a cup of tea to wash them down life would have been rosy enough.

From the Command Post in the slit trench just behind the guns came the G.P.O.'s shout:

"More four degrees . . . Two-thousand-four-hundred . . . Five rounds gunfire . . . Fire. . . ."

Keren Kate had just despatched the last of her five rounds when the bombardier in charge of the A.A. Bren-gun behind them began to blow his whistle in short blasts. Scanning the sky with his field-glasses he had spotted a score of Stukas heading towards them out of the sun.

"Take cover . . ." roared the G.P.O.

The gunners fled into their slit trenches. In a few seconds D sub-section, like the others of the Troop, were undergoing something far beyond their experiences in Death Valley. For the first time they heard the nerve-shattering screams of the Stukas as they dived steeply down from the top of the sky, making, so it seemed, straight for their trench. Involuntarily they ducked their heads lower to avoid the impact. One after another the Stukas hurled themselves from the skies without opposition. No sooner had one plane finished its dive than the next was on its way. The air was ripped by the incessant shrieks of the descending bombers, and buffeted by the tremendous blows of the exploding bombs. In their slit trenches the crouching gunners were rocked every now and then as if by some subterranean convulsion. For a time the novel, unearthly nature of the din silenced them. But after a minute or two, finding themselves still intact, they began to express in crisp, unfettered language their views on Stukas and what they would like to do to them. The Sergeant took a kindlier view.

"I'll forgive 'em," he said, "if only they let our sausages alone."

In his anxiety to know the worst he took a peep over the edge of the trench.

"Can't see a bloody thing for dust and smoke," he announced, ducking his head sharply in deference to the approaching scream of yet another Stuka.

The attack lasted for nearly ten minutes. When it was over their world seemed full of an unnatural silence. It was a minute or two before they could get used to it. Still dazed and half-deafened they clambered out of the trench and returned to the gun-pit.

It was hardly recognisable. And in the centre of the desolation of shattered sand-bags stood Keren Kate. She was hardly recognisable, too. She had received a direct hit. The trail was badly buckled, the carriage toppling over, and the piece blown sideways to an absurd angle. A lump of the muzzle had disappeared entirely. The tyres were ripped clean off. The dial sight had vanished. Half the range-drum was missing. The sight clinometer was gone. The elevating handle looked as if it had been sliced off with an incredibly sharp knife. The gun was deeply buried in the earth as if the bomb, not content with killing Keren Kate, had determined to push her into her grave also.

There she stood, a fit subject for laughter or tears. You could laugh at the ridiculous caricature of a 6-in. howitzer which Keren Kate presented in her drunken attitudes. Or you could weep at the sad contrast with her former gallant estate. D sub-section did neither. They stood grouped round this distorted version of their old companion eyeing it in silence. Sticking up on the front of the tilted carriage was her name, still vivid in white letters on a green square, untouched by the blast from the bomb. But for this the gun crew might have found it hard to believe they were looking at the same gun with which they had won laurels in Death Valley. She had been their staunch associate in many a grand shoot. Maybe they were remembering it now, not without some pang that the partnership was broken for ever. And maybe they remembered, too, that dreadful day when, grease-smothered, she had first arrived from Ordnance and had fallen to their lot. If so, they were in the mood to forgive her everything.

" We'll never fire that gun again," observed the Sergeant finally to the Limber-gunner. " We can remove the lock. That's all there is to salve."

The Limber-gunner made no reply. Of all D sub-section he found it hardest to come by words. Alone, he took a step nearer to the gun and stood gazing thoughtfully down upon the white letters of the name which he himself had once so proudly painted on the carriage.

Keren Kate . . .

" She never disgraced herself . . . She never let me down . . ." he said at last, addressing no one in particular.

" Knocked out . . ." he continued, after a pause. " Knocked out . . . But by a superior type of weapon."

He was shaping her epitaph. And also, for the last time, championing her against all detractors.

The Sergeant, far too ravenous to spend time sentimentalising over smashed-up howitzers, hastened away to the Primus stove, accompanied by the bombardier.

" Thank God, the superior type of weapon hasn't knocked out the sausages," he exclaimed.

They were still sizzling in the bottom of the petrol tin, though covered with powdery sand. The Sergeant helped himself to one and began to brush the grit off.

" Limber's pretty knocked out, himself," observed the bombardier sympathetically. " He doted on that gun. It'll be a long time before he forgets it."

" No," said the Sergeant, emphatically. " You've got to lay closer than that. You don't know limber-gunners as I do. Give him a new gun and an hour afterwards you'll hear him shouting the odds about it. It'll be the best gun that ever came out of Ordnance. Keren Kate ? . . . Why, he'll have forgotten all about her. Fickle's the word. Limber-gunners have to be like that if they're any good. . . ."

The Sergeant paused for a moment, reflecting.

" But there's one man that won't forget Keren Kate in a hurry," he said.

" Who's that ? "

" Me."

The bombardier could not conceal his incredulity.

" I never thought *you* were soft about her, sarge," he confessed.

" Soft ? . . ." echoed the Sergeant, grimly. " No. Not soft. . . . But I know I'm going to remember for the rest of my life the gun that knocked me off the ramp into that bloody river. The Old. . . ."

He checked himself sharply.

" Well, I won't speak ill of the dead," he said.

II—Début of a Pheasant

Strict wireless silence had been imposed upon the whole area of the Mareth Line. It was a highly necessary precaution. Stories of German skill in picking-up and de-coding messages had become almost legendary. So when, in response to a summons, N-Troop Commander of the 6-pounder anti-tank gun regiment appeared at Battery H.Q., the Major handed him the message-form with the casual remark :

" A Don R. brought it in from Corps H.Q. a few minutes ago. The Colonel sent it up."

The Troop Commander read the message, cocked an eyebrow at the Major, and read it again.

" *Collect four pheasants with beak at. . . .*"

There followed the map reference of a spot about twenty miles behind their gun positions.

The Troop Commander was a tall, thin-faced man, approaching forty, possessed of a countenance not easily disturbed into betraying his thoughts, let alone his feelings. He conveyed the impression of a man with a nicely-adjusted balance fitted just behind his forehead, on which he scrupulously weighed everything before passing judgment. His grey eyes, shrewd and humorous, shewed a faint trace of battle-weariness in their depths. Which was not surprising after five months of incessant fighting over the fifteen-hundred miles between El Alamein and Tunis.

He took another glance at the message-form.

" What's the dark mystery, sir ? " he said, amused. " Pheasants, I can understand, although it's their close season now at home. Here in Tunis the birds may not be so particular. . . . But ' Beak ' ? . . . I know we are low in rations. But what could we do with the beak ? "

The Major laughed.

" ' Pheasant,' " he elucidated, " stands for the much-rumoured and much-belauded new tank buster. Seventeen-pounder. . . . ' Beak ' is the ammo for the same."

" So it has actually materialised at last ! That's one up

to Rumour, lying jade. . . . Seventeen-pounder. . . . A big jump forward for us. I wonder whether it will be any good."

" It's a miracle-worker, by all accounts."

" It always is, sir," replied the Troop Commander, dryly.

" Well, you're to have the honour of the first sight of her. Get as many men as you require and take your four guns down to the Supply Point. They'll hand over four ' pheasants ' in exchange. In case of being spotted better bring up the guns in the twilight. The moon doesn't rise till fairly late."

The Troop Commander departed to make preparations for his journey.

For two days the six-pounders had been dug-in and sand-bagged on the desert not far from the little Tunisian town of Medinine, whose white, flat-roofed French and Arab houses were plainly visible from the positions. The gunners looked forward over their three-mile of front to the ridge that marked the line where the Germans were massed in the hope of resisting any farther encroachment by the victorious Eighth Army upon their fast shrinking foot-hold in North Africa. Only five hundred yards in front of the anti-tank guns the British infantry were dug-in, in four defence lines.

" We never have any luck," had grumbled N-Troop gunners.

Being so close-up to the infantry meant that the men had to live all the time in slit trenches. Such seemed to have been their fate ever since leaving Alamein.

The Troop Commander collected a sergeant and two men from each gun, hooked the six-pounders on to four Morris ' quads ' and started off on his errand. Upon reaching the Supply Point he was welcomed by a young Ordnance Captain who conducted the party to the corner of the artillery park where, suitably dispersed, their four ' pheasants ' awaited them, smothered in mineral jelly like thick axle-grease.

" There they are . . . A couple of brace . . . Beauties . . ." exclaimed the Ordnance Captain, enthusiastically.

The first thought of the Troop Commander was : " What a size ! . . ." Both in height and length the new guns compared with those he had been using for so long, looked colossal. He thought of the extra work it would entail on the men in digging-in. For an anti-tank gun it was of primary importance to be well dug-in and camouflaged so as not to betray its position by gun flashes. Otherwise, if you happened to miss first time the likelihood was that you wouldn't get a second chance. He judged from the remarks behind him that the Sergeants' first impressions had been similar to his own, though more forcibly expressed.

"That's the little devil that's going to make tank-busting like knocking off flies," continued the Ordnance Captain, rising to his theme.

"Glad to hear it," said the Troop Commander, mildly. "I hate flies."

"You needn't have any doubts. It has come out to us with the finest of credentials. It's a marvel."

"I'm not saying it isn't. And I'm not saying it is . . . yet," the Troop Commander replied. "But I do say that the way a gun behaves on some testing-range in the wilds of England isn't necessarily the way it will behave in the thickly-populated area of a tank battle."

The Troop Commander was not to be called sceptical. Much less, cynical. But he had reached a stage when he was loth to admit that a fact was a fact until it had proved itself right up to the hilt. His recent education had taught him this much, if nothing more. Twice—in the push under Wavell and in Auchinleck's offensive next year—he had assisted in driving the enemy out of Cyrenaica. Out for good, he each time confidently believed, like so many others. Twice he had found himself back, much to his surprise, in Egypt. Now for a third time, he had helped to push the enemy out of Cyrenaica. And not only Cyrenaica, but out of Tripoli also. A gigantic and inspiring push . . . He admitted that the auguries were better than ever before. There was the great weight of men and material: the shattering predominance of the R.A.F.; the thunderbolt genius of Montgomery. Nevertheless the mark of his previous lessons remained on him. He no longer felt inclined to jump to conclusions about anything.

The Ordnance Captain continued to sing the praises of the 'pheasant'. The Troop Commander let him have his head for a bit, keeping his own cool, though impressed by the other's obvious talents for salesmanship.

"Tell me about its snags," he interrupted at last, pleasantly. "I won't believe it hasn't any. It wouldn't be a gun if it hadn't . . . Don't think I'm biased. But I'm very attached to the six-pounder. I've always found it a grand little weapon. Efficient, and rarely fails to do a good job. I've never known a misfire. Good enough for any tank I've ever seen. So I'm a bit critical of this overpowering rival till she has shewn her paces. What are her weak spots?"

"I have heard a rumour that she has a flash as long as the gun itself," the Ordnance Captain admitted. "It's probably an exaggeration."

"Not too good," observed the Troop Commander, thoughtfully. "Anything else?"

"It's said to kick up a lot of dust."

"Also not too good."

He took another walk round the guns eyeing them attentively.

"What are they doing on those Mark I chassis?" he asked. "That's the 25-pounder carriage."

"Yes. We've had to mount them as best we could. Their own carriages were lost in transport. Torpedoed, I expect."

"Again, not too good," said the Troop Commander. "It means we shall only get a small traverse."

Having completed his examination of the bore, the breech, and the spares of each individual gun the Troop Commander passed on to the ammunition dump. The lieutenant in charge introduced him to his stuff, in boxes each containing two shells.

"Very nice-looking indeed," agreed the Troop Commander. "But I only see A.P. (armour piercing). Where's the H.E.?"

"There isn't any."

"A bit of H.E. comes in handy, you know, in the event of infantry supporting a tank attack," said the Troop Commander, gently. "Still, if there isn't any . . . No trailers, either?"

"No."

The Troop Commander went into consultation with his sergeants.

"We'll have to load the ammo into the quads," he said. "And there's the extra weight of the gun and carriage to be considered. It's going to entail a big strain on the tow-bar. So we mustn't overload."

In the end it was decided to load up thirteen boxes, containing twenty-six rounds, on the back of each quad.

"Get the guns cleaned up sufficiently so that we can use them if we are attacked on the way back. Concentrate on the breech and the bore. We shall be moving-off as soon as it is dusk."

Just before twilight the sergeants reported that all was ready for a start. The guns were hooked-in and the ammunition loaded. The Troop Commander signed a chit for the four 'pheasants' and received one from the Ordnance Captain in exchange for his 6-pounders. He was also handed several copies of the booklet describing the new gun.

"Haven't you anything about the drill?" he asked, taking a rapid glance through the booklet. "This is only technical."

No, there was no drill book.

"I see . . . We'll have to teach ourselves. If Jerry gives us time . . . Well, thanks for a very pleasant time, And I only hope that all you've told me about the gun comes true."

They were back at the battery in advance of the moon. Everything was quiet in front so the Major and the other three Troop Commanders had leisure for an inspection of the gun that had for so long been the subject of breath-bated rumour. The telescope was examined and passed with honours. The beautiful finish of the breech was admitted unreservedly. It was agreed that the ammunition looked of high quality. The small amount of traverse allowed them by the 25-pounder chassis was not appreciated so much. Still, studying the specification booklet in the light of the rising moon, it was generally agreed that there was much to be said for the 'pheasant' even before the bird had risen. The absence of a drill booklet did not matter considerably as, on closer investigation, the training seemed not to differ greatly from that of the 6-pounder.

"What did you pick up about her at the Supply Point?" the Major inquired of N-Troop Commander when the officers had gathered for a conference in the slit trench in the middle of the battery positions, which was B.H.Q.

"Wonderful things, sir . . . And some not so wonderful."

"Oh? What?"

"There's a rumour that she has a flash as long as the gun itself."

"The devil! . . ." exclaimed one of the Troop Commanders. "That'll make her a gift to any tank 'sitting back'."

"It means we'll have to pay extra attention to defilading," said the Major. "More than we've been doing with the 6-pounder. We'll have a much bigger flash to obscure . . ." He turned to N-Troop Commander. "Any other horrors?"

"I was told she kicks up a great deal of dust, sir."

"I'm not surprised to hear that. The important point is, will the dust clear in time for the layer to get in a second shot? That's a vital question. And something we shan't know till we are in action. Anyhow, I think it will be advisable for the Number One on each of the new guns to change his position. Instead of standing at the rear, as with the 6-pounder, he'd better move to the flank, and windward of the gun. That may help to counteract the dust. He'll have more chance of observing, and giving a fresh correction."

There followed a discussion as to the position of the 'pheasants'. It was decided not to mount them in the old pits vacated by the four 6-pounders.

"If, as warranted, they are effective at twelve-hundred yards as against our present six-hundred," said the Major, "it would be foolish not to take advantage of the extra range, and take on tanks in the rear of the attack."

So it was finally determined to place the 'pheasants' in positions behind the remaining 6-pounders of the battery, from two-hundred yards to four-hundred yards behind, according to the nature of the ground. The work had to be done immediately. An enemy attack might be put in at any moment. Throughout the night the gunners dug without a halt, while the limber-gunners finished off the job of cleaning up the guns ready for action.

By the time the 'pheasants' were all bedded-down and N-Troop Commander was satisfied that the defilading was good enough to obscure the tell-tale flash, dawn began to break. A dawn rosy and warm-looking in the cloudless eastern sky, but not so warm and rosy on the ground. It was bitterly cold, with a bleak wind blowing. Even in their mufflers and great coats the men found themselves shivering. Breakfast under these conditions, and after a hard night's digging, became considerably more than a mere meal. Each gun in the Troop did its own messing. The weary crews gathered behind the four new gunpits round the No. 2 cooking-stoves, which have the advantage of cutting out flame and fumes, and revived their energies with tinned bacon and bread washed down with copious draughts of strong tea. The bread was by way of a luxury. They were lucky to get it when they did. The ration had just come up.

The morning got under way and the air was beginning to warm up a bit when N-Troop Commander was summoned to Battery H.Q. On his arrival he found the three other Troop Commanders already huddled in the slit trench along with the Major, who had just raced back in his jeep from Regimental H.Q. situated in a small wadi, half-a-mile distant. One glance at the Major's face was sufficient to indicate that this was no mere domestic conference. So the Troop Commander was not surprised when he was greeted with the remark:

"We shan't be long now before we know what sort of birds those 'pheasants' are."

"Big news, sir?"

"Yes. Brigade H.Q. have just sent an urgent message to the C.O. There is a report in from Tactical Reconnaissance that the enemy have been observed concentrating armour at . . ."

He gave the map reference and the four officers carefully pin-pointed it on their map boards.

"It is expected Jerry will be launching the attack within the next couple of hours," he continued.

"Then the birds have arrived just in time for the shoot. Very thoughtful of them," observed N-Troop Commander. "What's the weight of the attack likely to be, sir?"

"Between forty and fifty A.F.V.'s." (armoured fighting vehicles).

"Something on quite a grand scale. The birds will have nothing to complain of about their début. I hope they'll rise to the occasion."

"Are the guns all ready? . . . In position? . . . Fully manned? . . . Have you checked up on the ammunition? . . ."

"We are short of a man apiece on two of the guns, and two men apiece on the other section," said N-Troop Commander. "Casualties, sir!" he explained. "It can't be helped."

The Major turned to the 6-pounder Troop Commanders.

"I want to impress upon you all," he said, "not to be too impatient. Let the tanks come well in so as to give the 17-pounders a chance to prove themselves. In any case, don't open up before the usual six-hundred yards."

The conference broke up and the officers hurried back to their Troops. A slight and unaccustomed feeling of suspense went with N-Troop Commander, hardened though he was to tank attacks. He attributed this to his uncertainty concerning the forthcoming behaviour of his 'pheasants'. Less than eighteen hours ago neither he nor his gunners had so much as set eyes on the new gun. They had barely had time to strike up a nodding acquaintance with it. The size of it, as compared with the little 6-pounder, still struck them as colossal, an impression that had not in any degree been modified by their digging operations during the night. All the gun's mysteries, its good points and its defects, remained to be explored. And here they were with a battle right on top of them. A very big battle, too . . . The Troop Commander was by no means apprehensive. He was quite ready to see the Ordnance Captain's enthusiasm vindicated to the last exclamation mark. On the other hand, he was ready not to. He held the balance even. He just wondered what would happen . . . Nevertheless, as he made his way back to the gun-pits, he could not help feeling that if it had been a case of his trusty 6-pounders he wouldn't have been wondering at all.

With map-board under his arm the Troop Commander went the rounds of his four 'pheasants'. Sitting upon each gun in turn he gathered the crew round him, gave them all the information he possessed of the coming attack, and pointed out to them its probable direction, first on the map, and then on the ground itself. This was rendered simpler because the area immediately in front of the position had already been paced and measured by the sergeants when the Troop first dug-in three days previously.

"Reference, the high feature . . . Three o'clock . . . Half-a-mile . . . Wadi . . ."

He pointed towards an unmistakable rise in the ground behind the enemy line.

"Seen, sir . . . Seen, sir . . ." each man notified as he picked the feature up.

Having concluded his instruction the Troop Commander took a last look round the gun, saw that the ammunition boxes were ready behind the trail with the lids thrown open, and shouted:

"Take post . . ."

The crew sprang to the positions from which they must not stir while awaiting the attack however long it might be in coming. The Number One planted himself to the flank and windward of the gun for better observing, as had been arranged. The gun was loaded. The layer settled in his seat. The ammunition numbers knelt beside the open boxes. Camouflaged in a sandy colour, with bands of dark paint wound round the piece like the coils of a boa-constrictor, and with the camouflage net breaking up the lines of the shield, the 'pheasant' was all-primed for its début.

The Troop Commander had stationed himself by the forward gun. Not far to his left, and slightly behind was another of the 'pheasants'. The other brace were still farther to his left, under the command of a lieutenant. He was still conscious of the slight feeling of suspense, neither more nor less than before. But as time went on without any sign from the enemy he found himself becoming more and more impatient to have his curiosity satisfied.

He passed the time in desultory conversation with the Number One of the gun, and gathered from it that the sergeant's immediate concern was very much like his own . . . How would the gun shape ?

It was not till an hour later that, well to their front, they saw a cloud of dust begin to rise from the ground.

" Here it is, sergeant," exclaimed the Troop Commander. " Same old circus."

He knew from past experience that they would not be setting eyes on any tanks just yet. It was the usual thing with Jerry before putting in a tank attack to swan about in the area for awhile, well out of gun range. These were intimidation tactics. They were specially designed to create an anxiety complex among the men in the front line, to make the waiting infantry jittery, and give the anti-tank gunners nerves so that the guns would not be laid accurately, or would open fire too soon and thus give the position away. The dodge was so well-known by now that the appearance of the dust cloud was merely taken by the gunners as an indication that they needn't bother themselves yet awhile.

For half an hour the parade went on without a tank becoming visible to the guns. Under the clear blue sky the battle area remained silent, except for an occasional tank shell bursting among the British infantry. It was a queer hush before the storm.

Suddenly the enemy artillery barrage opened. The shells began to drop heavily upon the infantry in their forward positions and screamed over the gunpits, bursting some distance behind. Recognising the symptoms the Troop Commander ensconced himself behind a low hummock of sand and, his tin-hat just showing over the top, commenced to observe the front attentively through his field-glasses. He knew he would not have to wait long now.

Gradually the enemy tanks emerged from the recesses of the dust-cloud, dark, indistinct shapes at first, but becoming sand-coloured and distinct in outline as they drew nearer. At three-quarters of a mile the Troop Commander, fixed to his binoculars, could distinguish them fanning-out over the front. They seemed to swarm out of the wadi like bees from a hive. Tanks of all types. In a few moments the Troop Commander had recognised the Mark III, the Mark IV, and the Mark IV special, very heavily armoured, and carrying a bigger calibre gun than its sister. A little later, at the rear, he picked out a couple of Mark VI's, the redoubtable Tiger tank, fifty-five tons in weight and carrying 88 mm. guns.

"This is the acid test for the 'pheasants'. No doubt about that," he thought, grimly.

More and more tanks poured out of the dust-cloud and spread over the battle line. Tanks . . . But no sign of infantry. Remembering the absence of H.E. the Troop Commander felt relieved.

"Something like a party, sergeant," he shouted, with his glasses still levelled. "What's your count ?"

"I make it fifty-one, sir."

"Fifty-three," the Troop Commander corrected.

"It's the biggest party we've had, sir, since that sixty at Hill 63, near Bir Hakeim, just after Alamein," said the sergeant.

"You're quite right, sergeant. I hope we are going to enjoy it."

"So do I, sir."

"You've spotted those two Mark VI's, sitting back ?"

"Yes, sir."

"Keep an eye on them. They may be dangerous. It's up to the 'pheasant'."

"Yes, sir."

The tanks were now coming in closer. They were easily distinguishable to the naked eye. A buzz of disjointed comment sounded from the men in the gun-pit.

"That's a Mark III . . ."

"How many can you count ? . . ."

"Look at that one . . ."

"That's a Mark IV . . ."

"Here's one coming straigh for us . . ."

"Must be hundreds of them . . ."

Not a round had yet been fired by any of the anti-tank guns. They just remained quiet and concealed, letting the enemy tanks approach without opposition.

"Three coming our way, sir," shouted the sergeant.

" I see them," replied the Troop Commander. " Just wait . . . They may swan out of our arc."

Never taking his eyes off the approaching tanks for a moment he continued calling out at short intervals: " Wait . . . Wait . . . Wait . . ."

As the attack was not being supported by infantry the British infantry themselves began to fall back. Had it been otherwise they would have had to stay and take their chance. Soon they were streaming back in scores, at a hurried walking-pace, crouching low, carrying their rifles and Bren-guns. Orange flashes were continually spurting from the tanks as they shelled the retiring troops and swept them with a heavy machine-gun fire. In a few minutes the infantry began to flow through the gun positions to their own alternative positions in the rear. Every now and then a handful of them would show a disposition to pause for a little back-chat with the gunners. They were peremptorily dealt with by the Troop Commander, fearful of having his position given away to the periscopes of the enemy.

" Keep moving, there," he kept on shouting. " Damn you . . . Keep moving."

The battle began to work up to its crescendo. But the crescendo was still all on one side. The artillery barrage had lifted and the tanks rolled forward in a wave of dust, detonating reports, and gun-flashes. Their shells began to kick up the earth in front of the gun positions. They were now drawing near to the six-hundred yards limit which was the usual opening range for the 6-pounders. In the Troop Commander's arc of fire this distance, which had already been paced out by a sergeant, was indicated by a solitary bush, a distinctive feature which none could fail to pick up. Their own particular customer, a Mark III, was now approaching the bush at a speed of fifteen miles an hour.

" Not just yet, sergeant," the Troop Commander called out.

" No, sir," replied the sergeant, in a cool, matter-of-fact tone.

Just then another tank reached the six-hundred yard limit of the nearest 6-pounder. Instantly the gun opened fire. Watching attentively the Troop Commander saw the shell crash fair and square in the centre of the turret.

"Grand little gun! . . ." he said aloud, in an outburst of pride in, and loyalty to the weapon that had served him so well in the past. The success of the 6-pounder had the effect of emphasising all the uncertainty in his mind as to the capabilities of her untried successor.

Along the whole front now the 6-pounders were coming into action. Mingled with their familiar crack the Troop Commander could hear a much heavier report, from which he guessed that his were not the only 'pheasants' making their début. It would soon be his turn. The Mark III was almost on a level with the solitary bush. He heard the voice of the sergeant at the forward 17-pounder suddenly shout:

"Take Mark III nearing bush . . . Lay . . . Six-hundred yards . . . Zero . . ."

The layer repeated back:

"Six Hundred . . . Zero . . ."

Quite unhurried, he took his time to lay on the approaching tank.

"On . . ." he shouted at length.

Almost immediately the Mark III reached the solitary bush.

"Fire . . ." roared the sergeant.

Flattened behind his hummock the Troop Commander drew in a deep breath. The moment had arrived. He kept a fascinated eye on the layer, watching his every movement. "He's had plenty of time to lay so he should be dead centre . . . if the gun fires accurately," he thought. He had a swift vivid picture of the layer with his hand on the firing handle. He saw him pull the handle. He heard the shell go. The crack seemed terrific after the 6-pounder's. A cloud of dust went up from around the muzzle.

Next instant he was watching the red streak of the shell's tracer speeding through the air. He noted the very flat trajectory. Owing to its high velocity the shell kept quite low to the ground. He followed its track. Suddenly the Mark III rose into his binoculars. He saw a small puff of smoke curl from the centre of the front of the tank, just beneath the turret.

The Mark III just stopped dead. There was no more firing. Not a sign of movement. From a giant of death and destruction it had passed in an instant to a giant of impotence. The red glow of flames began to show.

The Troop Commander felt the long burden of uncertainty and suspense drop from him. The delicately-poised balance in his mind went down with a bump in favour of the 'pheasant'.

"Beautiful! . . ." he exclaimed, with joy. "A grand little gun . . ."

It was the measure of his satisfaction that, unconsciously, he fell into the same words as he had used a few minutes previously to express his complete confidence in his old and well-tried friend the 6-pounder.

At the same time he became conscious that the sergeant of the 17-pounder on his left was giving a fresh correction to his layer. That meant he had missed with his first shell. Tank-busting being the sort of game where you can never count for certain on a second chance, the Troop Commander did not like the sound of it at all. He turned his head to watch proceedings in the gun-pit. He saw the fresh range put on, the layer re-lay, the gun re-loaded.

"Fire . . ." shouted the sergeant.

The layer pulled the firing handle.

Nothing happened . . .

"Great God! . . ." ejaculated the Troop Commander, aghast.

Misfire. . . .

Mechanical defect. . . .

The words leapt into his brain. But no more . . . Simultaneously there also leapt upon him a shattering explosion. Gun, gunpit, and all its contents disappeared beneath a shower of falling earth and stones and debris. The dust enveloped it like a shroud. A gloomy silence followed the crash.

It took the Troop Commander a few seconds to recover from the shock. When he could think at all he burst into an oath.

"Curse the bloody pheasant . . . It has cost me an entire gun-crew," he exclaimed bitterly.

There was no question now of eulogy, no kindly thoughts

in drawing comparisons with the six-pounder. The Troop Commander's scales had again bumped down. This time in the reverse direction. How right he had been not to be taken in by all that sales talk by the Ordnance Captain. . . . He only wished the fellow could be here to see the mess. . . .

He had no means of knowing what had happened inside the gun-pit, to cause the disaster, but he knew very well what had happened outside. He had spotted the Mark VI which did it. She was sitting back, stationary and aslant, eight-hundred yards to the rear of the line, evidently on the job of laying on gun flashes. She had seen the first flash of the 'pheasant,' laid on it and got a direct hit. The Troop Commander had noticed the flash from its gun almost simultaneously with the explosion in the pit. There had just been time for her to get in her shot owing to the ghastly failure of the 'pheasant,' he thought, with renewed bitterness. But for that she would probably have been smoking herself, by now . . .

Barely fifteen seconds had passed since the wreck of the gun-pit. The battle was still raging the whole length of the line.

"Engage Mark VI tank just to front," ordered the Troop Commander burning for vengeance, to the sergeant of the forward 'pheasant.'

"Engage Mark VI tank . . . Eight-hundred . . . Zero," the sergeant shouted.

"Eight-hundred . . . Zero . . ." repeated the layer.

It was a long lay although there was not much traverse. Eight-hundred yards was a big jump from the six-hundred they had been used to with the six-pounder. The seconds passed without the awaited signal from the layer. To the Troop Commander it seemed that he was never going to fire. But though consumed with impatience he knew the layer was right to take his time, and he was glad to find him cool and collected enough to do so.

Fully forty seconds elapsed before the layer finally shouted. "On . . ."

"Fire . . ." bawled the sergeant.

Off sped the shell. And it was then that the Troop Commander became aware that he had been half-expecting a repetition of the fiasco at the other pit. The sharp crack of the gun came almost as a pleasant surprise to him. So low had the 'pheasant' fallen in his esteem. . . .

Again he watched the flat trajectory of the shell through the air as indicated by the vivid red streak of the tracer following. He saw it hit the tank.

" A shade too high," he thought.

Nevertheless the Tiger ceased to fire. It stayed aslant of them as before, silent and dead.

Ten minutes later the battle was over. It had been a great début for the 'pheasants,' all along the line. Fifty-three tanks had emerged from behind the ridge. Fifty-three tanks now lay wrecked and blazing along the front. Not a single tank had got away. The majority just burned themselves out.

Now that the action was over the Troop Commander was able to render assistance to the casualties in the wrecked gun-pit. Of the crew of seven, three had been killed outright, and the other four severely wounded. After giving orders for them to be removed to the nearest casualty station the Troop Commander, accompanied by the sergeant of the forward 'pheasant,' went out to inspect the Tiger they had bagged. He was still not easy in his mind about the 17-pounder, despite the fact that the forward gun had a couple of tanks to its credit, including the redoubtable Mark VI. But the tragedy in the other gun-pit had deeply impressed him. He felt that he still wanted some more proof to clear up the uncertainty in his mind.

He found the required proof when he arrived at the lifeless Tiger and was confronted with the result of their hit. The shell had struck high in the side of the turret and torn a gaping hole. It had then, apparently, ricochetted inside and departed through the front. The driver had been killed by the shell itself, the other occupants by the concussion.

The Troop Commander stood surveying the shambles for awhile with keen interest.

" Pretty drastic, sergeant," he said.

The sergeant had no reservations at all to make as regarded the gun that had done it. He was enthusiastic. As enthusiastic as the Ordnance Captain.

" That was eight-hundred . . . And I believe, sir, we could do the same at a thousand," he concluded.

" Believe ? . . . I'm positive we could," said the Troop Commander with complete conviction.

III—The Quartermaster's Nightmare

" Desert warfare is the tactician's dream
and the Quartermaster's nightmare."
General von Ravenstein.

Dependable . . .

The word was writ large upon the Lieutenant-Quartermaster's solid exterior. You could read it at a glance. You read it in the level, unhurried gaze of the pair of wide-set grey eyes. You read it in the firm, reliable manner in which the square head was planted on the broad shoulders. You read it in the way his stocky frame, supported on large feet, gripped the earth, as if part of it, and equally to be relied upon.

Doubtless the Lieutenant-Quartermaster possessed more spectacular, more romantic qualities. But these were not so visible on the surface. Dependable . . . That was the conviction he inspired at first sight. And no poor recommendation for a quartermaster, either.

He was now seated in his office washing down a meal of bread-and-cheese and sardines with mouthfuls of scalding-hot tea. The Lieutenant-Quartermaster's office was a 3-ton truck with a camouflage net draped over its hood and a wireless aerial sticking up from the top. Its present position was a slight depression in the Libyan desert to the south-west of Gambut, and about a dozen miles from the hill known as Bel Hamid. Otherwise, the dusty, tawny desert stretched away pretty featureless on every side of him, except for the little hummocks of sand that had conglomerated round camel-thorn tufts. These be-sprinkled the desert so plentifully that it was impossible for vehicles on the move to avoid them, especially at night, and then a mile-an-hour became a good average pace.

Around the Lieutenant-Quartermaster's truck were dispersed, at distances of two-hundred yards between each, a fleet of soft-skinned vehicles. Water-wagons, ammunition-wagons, food-wagons, petrol-wagons. These comprised the B-échelon vehicles belonging to a 25-pounder battery attached to the 2nd New Zealand Division which, in the opening of the offensive of late 1941, was endeavouring to smash through Rommel's defences in the coastal area and link up with the British garrison that had been beleaguered in Tobruk for the best part of the year. The Quartermaster's battery had come through the wire with the New Zealanders south of Sidi Omar. They had assisted at the capture of the enemy supply base and aerodrome at Gambut, and had pushed on westwards to the hill of Bel Hamed, overlooking the ruined tomb known as Sidi Resegh, about twenty miles south-east of Tobruk. Here Rommel hit back with all the might of his Panzers. A great and ferocious tank battle developed, a fluid battle that slopped over miles and miles of desert; a battle in which masses of tanks careered all over the place attacking and counter-attacking; where, over a vast sea of sand, tactics bore more resemblance to those of a naval engagement than to anything previously experienced in land warfare.

It was noon on a day late in November. The battle of Sidi Resegh had already lasted nearly a week and showed no signs of diminishing in fury. As the Lieutenant-Quartermaster sat munching his bread-and-cheese he could hear the heavy gun-fire echoing all along a wide arc that swept down from the coastal area in front of him to somewhere many miles south-west of his position. It sounded to him as though the enemy was putting in a strong counter-attack from this direction. Possibly, he thought, it was the Italian Ariete Division which was believed to be somewhere in the El Gobi sector. He finished his hot tea, felt grateful to it, and also to the cardigan over his khaki drill shirt, for the weather was coldish. He wondered whether he would now have a chance of snatching forty winks before his next job came along. Most of the previous night he had spent bumping back over the desert after a dash forward with urgent water supplies to the battery, busily engaged, twelve miles away, knocking-out Panzers over open sights. He felt he would relish a nap.

"Message for you, sir," suddenly exclaimed one of the pair of wireless operators at the back of his truck.

The Quartermaster adjusted his earphones and seized his portable microphone, positive from experience that whatever form the message took it would certainly mean: "No nap." The operator switched from the receive to the send.

"Volo Six . . . Lieutenant-Quartermaster speaking . . . Over . . ." said the Quartermaster into the microphone, "Volo" being the code word for the battery.

In a few moments a distant voice was speaking back at him against a background of noise that the listener recognised as being the sound of the battery in action.

"Volo Six . . . Apples . . . Purple . . . Blue Gown . . ." said the voice, following up with the map reference of the battery's present position. "Over . . ."

"O.K. . . . Understood . . . Off . . ." replied the Quartermaster, writing down the message.

He reached for his mapboard, to the side of which was clipped the battery code. Deciphered, the message read: "Ammunition urgently required."

There was no need for him to be told the amount required, seeing that he was fully aware of the capacity of the guns. Working out the map reference he found that the battery had evidently shifted its position during the night. He would have a fifteen mile journey to make.

"Urgent job. The boys want some pills," he said to his driver, and spent the next twenty minutes driving around among the dispersed vehicles collecting into a small column all the ammunition wagons, six 3-tonners.

While the drivers were starting-up the Quartermaster busied himself working out with a protractor on the map the angle of the Forward Ammunition Point from which the much-needed 'pills' were to be collected. The F.A.P. was on wheels, and dodged about the desert according to circumstances. It consisted of about fifty R.A.S.C. lorries containing all kinds of ammunition for the needs of the

Division. Punctually every morning at ten o'clock the Quartermaster received from his battery H.Q. the map reference of the F.A.P. and marked it with a red spot on his map.

Emerging from his truck, he stood in front of it, and took a compass-bearing in accordance with the angle ascertained, laying the hair-line on a large camel-thorn bush that stuck up from a hump on the horizon. Finally he made a note of the reading on his speedometer.

By now everything was ready for the start. The Quartermaster stood up in his truck and held aloft a blue flag, the signal for " Follow me." The little column moved off in desert formation, staggered in pairs, in three rows, two-hundred yards between each vehicle. Kicking-up clouds of dust they swanned in the wake of the Quartermaster with their engines in second or third gear. Their pace was slow, barely five-miles per hour. But it was top pace in the desert because of the sand-hummocks and to save wear and tear on the springs.

After progressing at this crawl for an hour or so the Quartermaster glanced down at his dashboard. According to the reading on his speedometer they had come far enough and ought to be in sight of the F.A.P. He continued for another mile to the top of a low ridge and then hoisted a red flag. Behind him the column came to a halt. Standing up in his truck he began to sweep the desolation of the desert with his field-glasses. There was no sign of any F.A.P.—nothing but the interminable wastes of dirty-looking, powdery sand, coloured here and there with patches of bleached pebbles and the inevitable greyish-blue camel-thorn tufts.

" What in the name of hell has gone wrong now ? " he muttered.

Finally his gaze rested upon a small, distant, black object which did not seem to belong by natural right to the desert scene. Leaving the convoy halted he drove forward to investigate. He stopped his truck about sixty yards from the object and continued the journey alone on foot.

He walked up to a broken-down R.A.S.C. lorry, deserted except for its driver and a fitter who was engaged in removing sand from the carburettor.

"Are you part of the 2nd Division R.A.S.C.?" asked the Quartermaster.

"Yes, sir."

"Where are the ammo lorries?"

"Moved about three-quarters of an hour ago."

"Well, where are they now?"

"I can't truthfully say, sir," replied the fitter. "We got the wire that a marauding squadron of Jerry tanks might be expected any moment in this area. So the Captain thought it safer to move forward and get nearer Division. I had to stay behind to put this bastard in order."

The fitter pointed out the rough direction the F.A.P. had taken. The Quartermaster glanced at some tracks still fresh in the sand. It did not please him to notice they were at right angles to the way he had come, and led westward towards the direction of Bel Hamed and Tobruk. A couple of hours vital to the battery had practically been thrown away. All the time he could hear in the distance the sound of heavy gunfire along the whole of the western battle area. It sounded like very big business, and did nothing to allay his impatience.

Hastening back to his truck he rejoined the convoy and, with the blue flag, set them in motion again. He led them on the course indicated by the fitter. The tracks rapidly disappeared, obliterated by the wind-blown sand, and soon it became mere guesswork. They bumped along for another hour without seeing any trace of the F.A.P. Again the Quartermaster stood up in his truck and raked the desert with his binoculars. After a steady scrutiny he detected a small dust cloud on the horizon and made for it, hoping for the best. When within a couple of miles of it he halted the column under cover of a low sand ridge and went forward alone to reconnoitre. In a little while he was able to distinguish a couple of tanks. Studying them carefully through his glasses he came to the conclusion they were German Mark III's. The gun looked too big for the 2-pounder of the British Matildas and cruisers. More like a 6-pounder. Their turrets were heavier, too. And he could see the characteristic bogie wheels on top of the tracks.

"Get moving . . . They're Jerries . . ." he shouted to

his driver. And as though to remove any possible doubt about it a shell suddenly burst some hundreds of yards in front of them, raising a plume of sand and smoke.

They drove back to the convoy at record speed for the desert, and once more took up the chase of the Forward Ammunition Point. The Quartermaster now steered a more northerly course to keep well out of the neighbourhood of the enemy tanks. He bore this enforced deviation philosophically because he was now certain he had been on a wrong tack anyhow. He reasoned that if it had been otherwise the Jerry tanks would have already dealt with the F.A.P. in their path and he would have seen the black smoke from burning cordite and heard the explosions of the ammunition. He was happy in fact, to know that this time he had been travelling in the wrong direction. Nevertheless the waste of another precious hour or more was not a pleasing thought. Decidedly, he was now getting anxious.

He put on his earphones.

" Get me the Battery Commander," he told the operator.

" Q. speaking," he said when contact had been made. " Am on the way . . . F.A.P. has moved since this morning . . . I'm looking for them now . . . Do you know where they are ? "

" No," replied the Battery Commander. " I'll inquire of Division."

All the time they had continued to move steadily forward in a direction that was bringing them nearer the battle-zone. The gunfire seemed to be increasing in weight. After traversing another couple of miles, topping a rise in the ground, they came in sight of some fifty vehicles dispersed over the desert, a couple of miles away.

The Quartermaster shot up his red flag and the convoy halted. Standing up in his truck he focussed his glasses on the vehicles in front of him. And as he gazed a gladness filled his heart. At last, the F.A.P. . . . There could be no doubt about it. He could make out the stone-coloured scrim on the camouflage nets. The Jerries used dark blue scrim. On the backs of some of the vehicles he could distinguish the Divisional sign. And there was the pennant flying from the R.A.S.C. Commander's truck.

" Message for you, sir," shouted the operator.

The Battery Commander was coming through with the new map reference of the F.A.P.'s position.

"I've just found them," replied the Quartermaster.

"How long will you be? It's very urgent," said the Battery Commander.

"I shall do my best," the Quartermaster said, modestly.

"Good enough for me, Q," the B.C. declared, with a comforting and flattering confidence.

The Quartermaster headed his truck through the scattered vehicles of the F.A.P. towards the flying pennant. As he drew near, the Commander himself, a Captain, walked up to meet him. The Quartermaster hailed him with a joyous shout of recognition.

"You, of all the old scroungers," he exclaimed as they shook hands heartily.

Earlier in the year the pair had spent a riotous and never-to-be-forgotten leave in Cairo. As was the way with these Cairo intimacies they had parted when their leave came to an end, swearing eternal friendship and never expecting to see one another again.

"A bit different from last time, Harry," laughed the Captain.

"Yes. Business as usual, now," said the Quartermaster. "I want some ammo . . . Quick."

"How much? . . . What sort?"

"Eighteen tons of 25-pounder H.E."

"Any A.P.?" (armour-piercing).

"No."

The Captain indicated the lorries containing the 25-pounder stuff. The Quartermaster hoisted his blue flag and brought his convoy in. The vehicles backed tail-board to tail-board with those of the F.A.P.

"I'll give you half-an-hour for the job, and not a minute longer," the Quartermaster informed his sergeant.

"Have a drink while you're waiting," said the Captain, leading the way to his truck. He produced a bottle of whisky, unopened, and a couple of bakerlite tumblers.

"I see the R.A.S.C. don't go short," remarked the Quartermaster, with a grin.

"Things sometimes move in our direction," replied the Captain, blandly. "Any lime?"

" A drip or two. Neat whisky always catches me badly in the throat."

The Captain took his neat. They leaned against the truck, chatting.

" I've had a hell of a job finding you," said the Quartermaster. " Nearly got knocked-off by a couple of Jerry tanks. Did you see them ? They were probably looking for you."

" Division sent word they were in the area. That's why we moved in a hurry. Sorry you've had all the trouble."

" It's the battery I'm worrying about," said the Quartermaster. " They want this stuff badly. . . . Any news ? Isn't this bloody battle ever going to end ? "

" As far as I can gather we are just about holding," said the Captain. " I do know we are using up a terrific lot of ammo. Never known anything like it."

He replenished the tumblers.

" Here's to . . ." he said, drinking his off at a gulp before the sand could get at it. " Seen anything more of Cairo since ? . . . I haven't had the luck."

" I had a couple of days there before the push started," said the Quartermaster.

" Meet anybody nice ? "

" Yes. A French blonde at the Continental Savoy cabaret. A dream."

" Friendly ? " asked the Captain, with rising interest.

" Enough to give me her telephone number for future use."

" Have you got it now ? "

" It never leaves me," laughed the Quartermaster.

" Look here," said the Captain. " You might give it to me. I'm sure to get a spot of leave sooner or later."

" Wouldn't be fair to her," replied the Quartermaster. " She made me swear I wouldn't give it to anybody else."

" Oh, be dammed," cried the Captain. " They all say that. Just to flatter you. She'll be disappointed if you don't." He produced a pencil and pocket diary. " What is it ? " he demanded, hungrily.

The Quartermaster displayed an obvious reluctance to part with his treasure.

"She's pretty good, you know," he observed, thoughtfully.

"I can believe you, Harry," said the Captain with conviction. "I'm sure I shall like her."

"I mean she's too good to be, as it were, given away," continued the Quartermaster. "Given away for nothing."

"What's the idea?" demanded the Captain.

"Well, I think she's worth what's left of that bottle of whisky," the Quartermaster said firmly.

The Captain closed his diary with a snap.

"Not on your life!" he exclaimed vigorously. "That's all I've got till I find some more. All the women in Cairo aren't worth that to me when I've got the grit of this bloody desert biting my throat."

"But she isn't all the women in Cairo," protested the Quartermaster. "She's the one and only woman in Cairo, I assure you. Blue eyes . . . that lovely languishing look . . . skin like a peach. . . . And what a figure! . . . The sort described as serpentine . . . You know."

"Yes, I know," grinned the Captain. "Harry, old boy, you've lost."

On the stroke of the half-hour the sergeant doubled-up.

"All ready for moving-off, sir," he announced.

Back to serious business in a second, the Quartermaster cross-checked his position on the map with the Captain's, took the bearing of, and the distance to the battery with a protractor, and then "shot the desert" with his compass, fixing the hairline on a dip between two bumps on the horizon. Watching him attentively the Captain said seriously:

"If that's your course, take my advice and keep your eyes skinned. I hear there are likely to be Boche armoured cars out there between us and Division . . . With a detachment of motor-cyclist machine-gunners."

"I'm going straight on," replied the Quartermaster, simply. "I've got to take the chance. I must get this ammo up to the battery quickly. Already I'm behindhand, what with having to chase all over the desert after you. If there's any close trouble, well, I've got a tommy-gun, so some of us may get through."

He collected his drivers around him and showed them

on the map where they were and where they were making for.

" We've got to get this ammo to the battery at all costs," he said. " And without losing a minute. We may meet trouble on the way. So keep a look-out for armoured cars. . . . You know what to do if we are dive-bombed. Put a hard right, or left, lock on, and as you swerve jam your foot on the accelerator. But not too soon. Wait till he is on his dive."

Finally he got through to the Battery Commander.

" I'm on my way with the stuff," he said. " There may be trouble. If so I'll let you know."

" O.K. Be as quick as you can. Best of luck," was the reply.

He could hear from the noise on the set that the battery was in action again. Might have been in action all the time, for all he knew. The knowledge increased his anxiety to be off. He was just about to hoist his blue flag when the R.A.S.C. Captain thrust into his hand a bottle containing a liberal share of the whisky they had left.

" What's this for ? " grinned the Quartermaster.

" For love . . . For sheer love of you," the Captain laughed. " Take it, Harry. You may find it come in handy."

" Well, well, well. You white-whiskered old benefactor ! " exclaimed the Quartermaster in thanks. " Here, quick . . . Take this down. . . ."

He pulled out a pocket-book and read aloud a Cairo telephone number. The Captain gravely wrote it down in his diary on a page filled with similar entries.

" That also is for love," said the Quartermaster.

The convoy moved off on what the Quartermaster hoped would be the last stage. It was nearing sunset and to their right the distant clouds over the Mediterranean were taking on an almost awe-inspiring mixture of dazzling hues. Behind them the sky was deepening into a dark purple. The contrast was vivid and dramatic. But it evoked no æsthetic response from the members of the convoy. Not their eyes were alert, so much as their ears. Each man was listening intently to catch the first sound of the drone of an aeroplane engine, for this was just the time when the dive-bombers had a trick of suddenly swooping out of the sun, and were on top of you before you could spot them.

They travelled without incident for several miles, keeping steadily on their north-west-by-west course. The Quartermaster sat with the tommy-gun in the rack by his side. The gunfire grew louder with each mile they covered. The Quartermaster put on every fraction of speed he dared, hoping to make as much way as possible before darkness fell, which would happen immediately the sun set. The powdery desert dust swirled up in clouds round them.

Suddenly there was a whining sound and almost instantly a 75-mm. shell exploded with a terrific crack about fifty yards to their left. They had hardly recovered from the surprise when another shell—a 25-pounder—burst about the same distance from them on their right. Half-a-dozen of the same mixture quickly followed, some of the shells bursting close enough to send earth and stones slapping against the sides of the wagons.

The Quartermaster gritted his teeth. This was more than he had ever bargained for. Each of the six wagons behind contained three tons of high explosive and here they were, caught between the cross-fire of a couple of batteries, one Jerry and the other evidently British.

" Put on all you can," he shouted to his driver. " We've got to get out of this in a hurry, whatever happens."

The driver pressed his foot on the accelerator and the truck took a leap forward. Behind, the six ammo wagons followed suit. They bumped over the sand hummocks, rising and falling like boats on a heaving sea. Every now and then the Quartermaster found his head bouncing up to hit the hood of his truck. The shells continued to fall round them on both sides.

" What do you think has happened, sir ? " the driver managed to gasp out in the intervals of being bumped out of breath. " Fine game if we're being shelled by our own battery."

" It isn't quite as funny as that," replied the Quartermaster. " We are heading direct for the battery, and there's no shooting coming from that quarter. I think we've run into a sort of No Man's Land, and each side takes us for the enemy."

" Gives us a double chance, like," said the driver, glumly, as another two shells burst one on either side of them, and closer than ever before.

The Quartermaster did not reply. The " double chance," as the driver had so succinctly put it, was full of the most unpleasant possibilities. Sooner or later he felt sure something would hit them.

" Keep it going," he said. But their best speed seemed a poor thing in the circumstances.

And then, as suddenly as they had accumulated, his anxieties were lightened. The convoy had just safely weathered what might be described as a double salvo when the sun dropped beneath the horizon. Almost immediately darkness closed around them.

" Thank God for sunsets . . ." the Quartermaster exclaimed fervently.

Two or three more shells fell and then the shooting stopped altogether. All told, they had been the target for nearly thirty rounds.

" Slow down . . ." ordered the Quartermaster. His truck relapsed to a crawl. Behind him the convoy closed up for night travelling, forming a " snake," the vehicles nose to tail and only ten yards apart so as not to lose touch. The Quartermaster continued to steer for the distant sand hump, though he could no longer see it. He sat with his illuminated compass in his hand directing the driver.

" Straight. . . . Straight. . . ."

The driver held to the course by keeping a piece of white adhesive tape, which was stuck on the top of the steering wheel, upright all the time.

So they progressed for another five miles. The Quartermaster began to feel quite happy. They had evidently missed the armoured cars, the dive-bombers hadn't arrived with the sunset, and so far as he could judge, another ten miles or so would see them through. It had been a harassing job, full of exasperating delays, and he would be glad to see the back of it. On the whole he considered they had been lucky. He thought with what satisfaction he would in a short time be dumping his eighteen tons of H.E. at the battery.

All at once, above the noise of their own engines, he became distinctly aware of the drone of two planes.

"They must be pretty near to us to be heard so plainly," he said to his driver. He took a look up at the dark sky. At first he saw nothing. Then two small points of light appeared which developed into two white flares wafted towards them by the slight breeze, leaving a tail of smoke behind. At the same time the first three bombs fell, not very far away.

"They've spotted us . . ." he yelled to the driver. "Keep moving . . . Fast as you can . . ."

Once more the whole convoy began to pitch and toss about as it took the desert hazards at the top of its speed. The Quartermaster stood up on his seat and glanced back over the truck's hood to see how the drivers were taking it. He noticed with satisfaction that the rear wagon had temporarily halted, so as to enable the convoy to disperse while it was still on the move. Instead of being jammed tightly together his eighteen-tons of H.E. was already strung out behind him with fifty yards between each vehicle. He breathed a little more freely when he saw that.

The two Heinkels again circled round and dropped another stick of bombs. The fourth wagon of the convoy stopped dead, with a bomb splinter through the engine. This had the effect of halting the wagons behind. The sergeant who was riding in the rear wagon ran forward to investigate. He ordered the injured vehicle to be taken in tow with tow chains. The rest of the convoy tore on. Another stick of three bombs dropped but did no harm. It was the Heinkels' final effort. Five minutes later, in the light of the dying flares the Quartermaster had the pleasure of seeing the disabled wagon already moving slowly forward in tow.

He resumed his seat again, drawing a deep breath of relief. Now that the chance of their all going-up with eighteen tons of H.E. had passed he discovered himself to be in a muck sweat, although the night air was cold. He began to shiver so much that he donned his greatcoat. In the pocket he found the bottle of whisky the R.A.S.C. Captain had presented him with. At that moment he felt he could cheerfully have given the Captain the telephone numbers of all the serpentine blondes in the world.

When the bombing ceased the wagons had dropped back again to their normal place and closed up. Glancing down at his speedometer the Quartermaster saw that they had traversed another five miles.

"We ought to be hitting something of ours soon," he remarked to the driver.

Passing the word back to the convoy that he was going to halt, he descended from the truck.

"Wait here till I come back," he ordered his driver.

In the pitch darkness he set out to locate the battery. He anticipated that he might still have a mile or so to go, but no more. With the coming of night an uncanny hush had settled upon the battle area. He could not hear even desultory gunfire. The only noise that broke the stillness was the occasional distant grating of tanks changing their positions.

After stumbling along for a mile he was brought to a halt by a sharp challenge. A couple of infantrymen, armed with tommy-guns, confronted him out of the darkness.

"Who are you ?" they demanded.

The Quartermaster informed them.

"Where's your identity card ?"

They escorted him to a vehicle close by, within which they examined the identity card by the light of a torch and compared the photograph with the original.

"O.K."

"I'm looking for the 999th Regiment," said the Quartermaster. "Seen anything of them ?"

"Over there to the right . . . About a mile on," replied one of the men.

The Quartermaster was about to depart when the other man remarked:

"They may have moved. I saw some guns pulling-out from that direction some time back."

All the pleasant thoughts that he was soon to see the end of a very troublesome day retreated from the Quartermaster's mind. This was a contingency he had not foreseen. If it were true, then he would have to take up the chase of the battery again, in the darkness, and at the moment he hadn't the faintest notion where to look for it. Many, many hours had passed since he first received the message that ammunition was urgently wanted. Many more hours than he liked to count. He had done his best, but it was no use blinking the fact that the battery was still without its ammo. He hoped the Major wasn't thinking he had let them down. That would be a pity because the Major had always shown the utmost confidence in him . . . After all, perhaps he was worrying about nothing. The battery might not have moved.

He made his way back to the convoy. The towed vehicle had just been brought in. He inspected the damage and congratulated the sergeant and the driver on the job they had done. He could hear the water inside the radiator boiling, and steam was pouring out.

"Give it a blow," he ordered.

The driver turned the wagon head-on to the light breeze so that it could blow through the radiator.

Buoyed-up with hope the Quartermaster drove back in his truck towards the spot indicated by the infantryman. There was no sign of the battery. Only empty gun-pits. It was a bitter disappointment.

"They've gone . . ." he said abruptly. He turned towards the operator in the back of the truck. "Try and get the battery on the set, and let's find out where they are," he ordered.

He adjusted his earphones while the operator got busy.

"Volo Six calling Volo . . . Volo Six calling Volo . . . Over . . ."

Anxiously, the Quartermaster waited. He listened hard for three minutes. There was no reply.

"Try them again," he said.

"Volo Six calling Volo . . . Volo Six calling Volo . . ."

Another wait of two minutes and still no reply.

"What the devil can have happened?" the Quartermaster was thinking. "Why didn't they inform me they were pulling out? . . . They must have had to move damn quickly. . . ."

And he had a very depressing feeling that whatever had

happened to the battery might not be unconnected with the non-arrival of the much-needed ammunition.

Again the operator sent out his signal to the desert night:

"Volo Six calling Volo . . . Volo Six calling Volo . . ."

This time, when he switched to receive, the silence was broken. To his profound relief the Quartermaster heard a voice speaking:

"Volo answering . . . Volo answering . . . Over . . ."

"Where's the battery now? I'm at the old position," he asked the signaller at the other end.

When he listened again it was to the cheery voice of the Battery Commander himself.

"Is that you, Q? We had to move quick and are still moving on a bearing of . . . (the Quartermaster jotted it down carefully) . . . Is everything O.K.? . . . Over . . ."

"Everything O.K." replied the Quartermaster with a lightened heart. "Will follow you up . . . Over . . ."

"Be as quick as you can . . . Off."

The Quartermaster drove back to the convoy, comparatively happy.

"Start up . . ." he ordered.

While the drivers were making their preparations he jumped out of his truck and took a compass bearing in accordance with the Battery Commander's information. Once again the convoy began its slow crawl over the pitch-black desert. At the head of it in his truck the Quartermaster sat holding the compass in his hand with his eyes fixed all the time on the illuminated arrow.

"Right . . . left . . . left . . . right . . . hold it . . ." he continued shouting to the driver, thus keeping the truck dead on the bearing.

They bumped along for another three miles, in a south-easterly direction now, without sight of the battery. The night had turned much colder and suddenly the breeze developed into a strong wind. The sand began to whirl up and cut into the faces of the drivers, for the wagons were unprovided with wind-screens, a precaution against reflection of the sun's rays.

Soon the wind was bellowing above the sound of their engines. The night seemed to grow blacker than ever. Such few stars as had been visible were blotted out of the sky. The convoy lights that glowed faintly on the white differential beneath each vehicle were completely obliterated. In order to keep touch the wagons closed up till they were practically touching one another.

"Curse it! . . ." exclaimed the Quartermaster with all the venom he could summon up. "We're landed with a bloody sand-storm now . . . As if we haven't already had enough to put up with. God knows when the battery will get its ammo now . . . We may be blotted out for days."

He stood up in his truck and yelled down his megaphone: "I'm going to halt."

Behind him the convoy came to a gradual rest. There was nothing more to be done, except to make themselves as comfortable as possible and just wait till the storm blew itself out. That might be a matter of hours or days. The Quartermaster had the one consolation of knowing that the Battery was in the same boat as himself and therefore would not be breaking its heart for want of ammunition yet awhile. He ordered the wireless operator to get into touch with the Battery Commander.

"Sandstorm raging . . . Am staying put . . . Have come three miles . . . Over . . ." he said.

"I'm staying put, too," replied the B.C. "You are about six miles from us . . . Over . . ."

"O.K. . . . Off . . ."

Outside the sand was swirling more vigorously than ever, and the fierce blasts of wind drove it through every crevice of the vehicle with cutting force. The Quartermaster put on his sand-goggles. He could have done with something to eat, but it was useless to try. He would simply have been eating sand. He ventured upon a quick swig of whisky from the R.A.S.C. Captain's bottle, once more fervently blessed the donor, tied a handkerchief round his nose and throat, and fell asleep.

He awoke, stiff and cold, and smothered with grit, after what seemed to him but a brief nap. Glancing at his watch he found he had been asleep for six hours. The wind had dropped considerably but the sand still clogged the air. However, even as he stared out over the dark desert he could see that the fog was gradually subsiding.

Suddenly a single star appeared in the sky. And soon the atmosphere had cleared sufficiently for him to detect others. Unexpectedly the storm was over.

He was out of his truck on the instant.

" Start up . . . Moving . . ." he shouted to the nearest convoy driver. " Pass the word down."

At the same time, anxious to see how the vehicles had fared during the storm, he walked down the column inspecting the engines in case they were spluttering or " missing " as they would be if sand had entered the carburettor, and no petrol was getting through. Much to his relief only one engine failed to start-up. Considering the manner in which all the vehicles were covered with sand the Quartermaster considered himself very lucky to get off so lightly.

" A.3 has got petrol trouble," he said to the sergeant and fitter in the tail waggon. " You stay behind with her and follow us up as soon as you've got her going."

He gave the sergeant the compass-bearing of his course, returned to his truck, informed the Battery that he was on the move again, and recommenced his Odyssey, wondering grimly what new trouble he would run into before his job was done. He had only six miles to go, but his experience of the past fifteen hours had taught him, if he hadn't known it before, that in desert warfare a lot can happen to a Quartermaster in the space of six miles.

However, this six miles provided no surprises except at the very end when the Quartermaster, having checked the speedometer and found he had travelled the right distance, discovered himself to be alone with his convoy in the naked desert, with never a sign of the Battery. He halted the column and once again went off by himself in search of the missing guns. After scouting around in the darkness in every direction for a radius of a mile or more without finding anything to give him the slightest clue, he returned, cursing his fates, to his truck.

" They've done the vanishing trick on us again," he said to the wireless operator. " I'm beginning to think we'll still be found carting this cargo of ammo round the desert when the war is over. Get the Battery Commander on the set and let's find out what has happened this time."

"B.C. here, sir," announced the operator after a few seconds.

The Quartermaster adjusted his ear-phones.

"I've come six miles on the bearing you gave me and there's no sign of you," he said. "Where are you now?"

"I'll send up a tracer signal for you," was the reply.

Shortly afterwards the Quartermaster saw five red tracer bullets from a Bren gun streak up in quick succession into the dark sky from the desert over to his right. He could hear the gun reports, too. They seemed quite close. But he knew this was merely due to the way sound travelled over the desert at night. He took a new bearing on the tracers, put the convoy in motion again, and drove straight on it. At the end of another two miles there was still no sign of the Battery. The Quartermaster wasted no more time. He got through once more to the B.C.

"Give me another signal," he said.

In a brief while another five tracers shot up into the sky. Their bearing was the same as the one he was already travelling on, so he knew he was all right for direction. And as the reports sounded much louder than before he congratulated himself that he had run the Battery to earth at last. He drove straight on and after proceeding for a mile-and-a-half had the joy of bumping into a truck belonging to the Battery.

"Where's the Major?" he asked the driver.

"Up at the Battery position," was the reply.

"How far is it?"

"Three-quarters of a mile . . . Straight ahead."

The Quartermaster went forward on foot. He found the Major at the Command Post, a dug-out with slit trenches, chatting with the Command Post Officer and two Troop Commanders in from the O.P.'s.

The Quartermaster's stocky figure darkened the entrance to the dug-out.

"Is that you, Q?" asked the Major, glancing up.

"Yes, sir."

"Well done. I hardly expected you to find us so soon. Though I've been damned anxious that you should. Have a gin and lime."

"I'd have caught you before you moved if I hadn't

had to run all over the desert looking for that R.A.S.C. column," the Quartermaster replied, making short work of his drink. "Why the hell didn't Division let us know they had shifted."

"Probably couldn't find us for the moment. We had a bit of a party . . . Tank attack . . . We'd already supported a big infantry push and practically used up all the stuff. So we had to move quickly. At the present moment we haven't more than five rounds a gun left. So you can see how welcome you are. Did you get through with all the load?"

"Barring one truck that was knocked out in the sandstorm. I had to leave it behind for repairs. They know where to come."

"I'll send out a guide to make sure," said the Major.

There was a buzz on the telephone.

"Message from Division, sir," called the operator. "They want to speak to you."

It was some time before the Major finished with the earphones.

"That was to say we have to put down a box barrage commencing at dawn," he announced. "The infantry are putting in another big attack. Q, you've arrived just in time. But it looks as though you'll have to start back as soon as you've unloaded and do the same job all over again. These box barrages are the devil for eating up ammo. Have another drink before you go."

IV—"What is Written . . ."

The Assistant Surgeon himself volunteered the suggestion that it was time to shift to new quarters. Up till now the M.O.'s Office of the 25-pounder regiment had carried on comfortably enough at the foot of the hill-side. A stray shell or two had dropped in the vicinity, but nothing to worry about. The doctoring and poulticing went on more or less undisturbed. Then, without warning, a battery from another regiment moved in just behind. After that, conditions changed distinctly for the worse. The M.O.'s Office found itself constantly exposed to shell-fire from the Italian gunners across the valley. It interrupted work, and made things unpleasant all round.

When the Assistant Surgeon decided it would be a good idea to move to some more salubrious spot the M.O. had no objection to offer.

"All right," he agreed. "I don't mind. I can attend to disordered bowels and endorse sick reports 'Inflammation of the Ariola Tissue' anywhere you like. But you? . . . I always understood you were a tough fatalist," he added, with his fondness for twitting his staff on every possible occasion.

The Assistant Surgeon, tall, spare, with a brown complexion and brown eyes was an Anglo-Indian. He held the rank known in the Indian Army as Sub-Conductor, which corresponds closely to that of Regimental Sergeant-major in the Home Army. As is often the case with Englishmen who have spent best part of their lives in India he had acquired, in addition to the complexion of an Indian, a pronounced tinge of Oriental fatalism. "What is written is written . . ." was a phrase seldom absent from his lips for more than a day. Ever since the 25-pounder regiment, which was attached to the 4th Indian Division, found itself involved in the grim struggle for Keren, the M.O. had heard it quite a lot. Now he heard it once more.

"I'm thinking of the others, the sick parade. Not of myself," the Assistant Surgeon went on to explain.

The M.O. nodded. "Start as soon as you like," he said.

For seven weeks the regiment had been in the valley facing the heights of Keren. Black, forbidding mountains with sheer rock faces, deep gorges, and needle-peaks shut them in on three sides. A few gloomy spruce trees here and there, and patches of dark mosses, provided the sole relief to the harsh bare rock of precipitous clefts and violent slopes. The guns were dug-in at the foot of a mountain in the sandy, boulder-strewn bed of a dried water-course alongside the Agordat-Asmara road. Such cover as they got was provided by a few gaunt, black trees, with great hollow trunks topped by rigid, distorted branches, and utterly devoid of any foliage whatsoever. They had a petrified look about them, as though belonging to the mineral rather than to the vegetable kingdom. The gunners dug deep under the arched and twisted roots and bedded-down amongst them. Over this inhospitable scene there hung, day after day, a torrid, brooding sky that rendered the atmosphere in the valley as sultry as if threatened with a tremendous thunderstorm.

The fauna of the valley possessed for the gunners a variety lacking in the flora. But it could not be fairly described as more lovable. Black and grey rock-snakes, six-feet long and two-inches in diameter, climbed the bare trees and had an objectionable habit of dropping down at unexpected moments upon the men below. These snakes were very poisonous. As an off-set, they were warranted not to bite unless attacked first. But when a six-foot snake suddenly lands on your back from nowhere, it is a neat point as to who is the aggressor. The gunners used to trap them with forked sticks and play with them during a lull in the firing. Black scorpions, nine inches long, provided a change of amusement. They crept in among the blankets in the tree roots and stung the sleeper without waiting for provocation. The result was an unpleasant headache all next day. They were altogether unprepossessing creatures, with their crab-like movement, ugly pincers, tapering body, and jointed bulbous tail. Here resided the sting. They whipped the flexible tail swiftly over the back and stung as they were in the act of drawing it away. By comparison with the scorpions the tarantulas, of which there was abundance, might be regarded as domestic pets. They resembled enormous spiders, six-inches long, with strong, hairy legs, and yellow and green bodies striped in black down the back. The tarantulas also showed a preference for the gunners' blankets. There were two pronounced schools of thought about them. One considered it unlucky to kill them. The other didn't.

By day, flocks of gaily-coloured parrots and parroquets, which nested in a small wood near the cook-house, flew screeching over the gun positions. By night, dog-faced baboons descended from the higher slopes of the rocks to rifle the battery kitchens, and added to the general eeriness of the surroundings with their half-human, half-unearthly yell, a long drawn out "Halloo . . . oo . . . oo . . . oo . . .," which echoed among the recesses of the rocks, and gradually died away like an expiring soul in torment. It was found necessary to keep an eye on the baboons, especially in the daytime. In the Battery H.Q. the order was posted :

"Any baboons caught photographing positions are to be brought to H.Q. or shot on the spot."

In its way this was a tribute to the daring and ingenuity of the native Eritrean troops taking part in the defence of the Italian mountain fortress. They made a practice of dressing-up in the skins of baboons and filtering down into the valley to reconnoitre the British lines. Just at the present moment it was more than ever vital that their activities should be curbed. A new attack on the rocky heights protecting Keren was about to be launched. Troops were massing in the valley, Sikhs, Royal Fusiliers and Skinners Horse. The Cameron Highlanders still clung to their precarious and hard-won foothold on Brig's Peak, together with the Punjabis. All the gunners of the 25-pounder regiment knew the attack was imminent. They had been mustered outside the Battery H.Q.'s and coached by their section officers.

"Should any of you have the misfortune to be taken prisoners you are not to say what your regiment is, or give any information about the positions," they had been told. "You may say that you belong to the Royal Regiment of Artillery. The enemy is entitled to know that. Also, if you are questioned about other troops you are to say that there are lots of Australians. There aren't any at all, we know. But the Italians have a holy dread of the Aussies and think there are. They've been misled by the slouch hats of the Garwhalis."

Meanwhile, as if in anticipation of the attack, the Italian heavy artillery and mountain batteries on the peaks opposite became more active than ever. It was at this moment that the Assistant Surgeon decided to move elsewhere.

The spot eventually selected by the Assistant Surgeon for the new M.O.'s office was higher up the hill-side, about three hundred yards from the battery position, and behind it. As the routine work of the M.O. could not be interrupted the change-over had to take place during the night. The Assistant Surgeon broke the news to the young Bombardier and the gunner who acted as his assistants. They had been seconded from one of the batteries to help the M.O. because they happened to be the only people who possessed any first-aid qualifications. There were no R.A.M.C. orderlies available, though the hospitals at the rear were staffed with native Indian orderlies.

The Bombardier was quite fed-up with the job. His one anxiety was to get back to his gun. And the news of the impending attack had the effect of making him more restless than ever. Sitting chatting to a couple of other bombardiers that evening outside R.H.Q. Officers' Mess, he made no secret of his grievances. His companions heartily sympathised with him.

"I'm bloody glad I didn't have any first-aid qualification," said one of them. "Messing about with sand-sores day after day would take my appetite away. I'd sooner see a good, hearty shell wound. I think I'd sooner get one."

The young Bombardier gloomily agreed. Sand-sore cases were the bane of his existence. He hated the sight of them. And there were dozens of them awaiting him on every morning's sick parade. It was a complaint very rife in the valley. The slightest cut or abrasion of the flesh developed into a great festering sore within the course of an hour. Iodine had proved useless as a treatment. The M.O. had concocted a special ointment to cope with the plague. It consisted mainly of M. and B. 693, and proved a great success. The sores soon healed and the new flesh grew quickly. It was one of the Bombardier's jobs to keep supplies going. Every morning, before sick-parade, he pounded up a large tinful of the white mess. And if there was one thing on earth he hated more than the sight of sand-sores it was the sight of sand-sore ointment.

"I'll have to tell the M.O. I want to get back to the Battery," he said. "Not that I have any great hopes.

You know what he's like. Always turns everything into a joke. I bet that his only reply will be: 'Get off your knees.'"

"What's the idea?"

"The Assistant Surgeon makes him feel short. So he likes to point out that he's taller than me, though there's barely an inch difference," explained the Bombardier, who was a stocky little fellow with abbreviated legs. "It's a joke of his to pretend I'm so short that I must be walking on my knees. But he. . . ."

He was interrupted by a sudden yell from the other.

"Look out! . . . He's got you. . . ."

From where he was sitting the young Bombardier took a dive forward on to the ground. He expected a rock snake, or, at least, a scorpion. As he leaped he felt his back brushed heavily by a sweep of his companion's hand. He recovered in time to see him stamping upon a huge tarantula. The Bombardier was dismayed. He belonged to the school that regarded it as unlucky to kill a tarantula.

"I don't thank you for that," he said. "There goes my chance of getting back to positions."

"Get off your knees," laughed his companion.

At seven o'clock the Assistant Surgeon, the Bombardier, and the gunner began the task of digging out a new office in the hillside. Most of the time it was very hard work, a pick and shovel job, for below the thin top layer of sandy earth they encountered sheer rock. It took them till one o'clock in the morning, by which time they had dug out a space about a stretcher-length each way. Over the entrance they hung a twelve-foot tent-cover to prevent the hot sun of the daytime from melting the unguents. This they smeared with old engine oil and then flung sand over it as a camouflage, and distributed a few spruce branches on top. Afterwards in the darkness, they made many journeys backwards and forwards between the old office and the new, transferring the medical panniers, bottles of drugs, surgical equipment, and stretchers to their future abode. The Bombardier's last job, in the early hours of the morning, was to paint a large three-ply board white with a big Red Cross, and to stick it up on a pole facing the Italian positions on the other side of the valley.

By eight o'clock, after a very curtailed night's rest, the M.O.'s staff were installed in their new quarters, making preparations for the morning's sick-parade. They had every reason to be satisfied with their efforts of the previous night. The new office looked workmanlike and ship-shape. Everything was just as the fastidious M.O. liked to find it. Over the M.O.'s table, constructed of empty four-gallon petrol tins, was spread a clean towel, with his stethoscope and orascope and a pair of rubber surgical gloves, wrapped in sterilised lint, all in their exact places. By the side of the table stood the two medical panniers, also covered with clean towels. On these were arranged bottles, jars and tins of various sizes which contained the drugs, pills and ointments. All were marked with clean, large, white labels. The M.O. was very particular about the labels. In one corner of the office a Primus stove was heating-up some water in a white enamel bowl containing the instruments to be sterilised. Close by, on an upturned petrol tin, kaolin poultice, lint, cotton-wool and bandages, were ready for fomentations. Alongside the opposite wall was a stretcher, supported by four petrol tins, one at each corner.

Considering the circumstances, especially the shortage of water, the general air of cleanliness and tidiness about the office which had sprung up, mushroom-like in a night, reflected great credit upon all concerned.

Shortly afterwards the M.O. himself put in an appearance, spruce as usual, in khaki shirt, shorts, sun-helmet and puggaree complete. In his hand he carried the horsehair fly-swat that he never moved a step without. He considered it a far more important piece of equipment than his tin-helmet, which he was accustomed to refer to contemptuously as his 'Dutch courage,' and never wore except in the greatest of emergencies. The M.O. had bought the fly-swat in Cairo. It was his dearest possession. And though by now its strength had been reduced to the measure of about half-a-dozen hairs his faith in its powers remained undiminished. But it was his disposition to be cheerful in all circumstances. And it was this quality, reinforced by his readiness to help anyone who was in trouble, irrespective of rank or colour, that had made him the most popular officer in the regiment.

The M.O. ran a rapid eye over his table, over the array of bottles on the panniers, and over the preparations on the Primus stove.

"Excellent," he exclaimed, in approval. "It reminds me of a surgery. I think we are going to be very comfortable here . . . I suppose you have heard the news? The attack is coming off to-morrow."

The Bombardier thought it a good opening for him.

"Could you arrange, sir, for me to get back to positions?" he asked. "I'd be very grateful."

"Ah, it's you, Bombardier. I didn't notice you. What are you doing on your knees, man?" replied the M.O. in his bantering mood.

A vision of a squashed tarantula appeared before the Bombardier. He already considered his chances hopeless. But he made another attempt.

"I'm very anxious to get back on the gun, sir," he pleaded.

"I know you are," said the M.O. sympathetically. "But I can't possibly let you go just now. Your services are far too valuable to me. What should we do without you? But wait till Keren falls. Then we'll see what can be done about it."

"I'm waiting for that, too," said the Assistant Surgeon. "And I hope that I haven't got to wait much longer."

They all knew why he spoke so fervently. He was craving for a glimpse of his baby daughter, born after he had left India for Egypt, and now fifteen months old. His favourite topic was this baby that he had never seen. His wife had brought the child to Cairo, and rarely a week passed without the Assistant Surgeon receiving three letters from her all devoted to satisfying his hunger after details concerning the baby. He would long ago have gone on leave, but for the obstinate resistance of Keren. All his hopes were centred on the downfall of the mountain fortress. He made no secret of it, though in general, he was a man of reserve. Even the Bombardier recognised that his own longing to get back to his gun was a puny thing by comparison with the intense desire that possessed the Assistant Surgeon.

"I shall certainly miss you," said the M.O. emphatically.

Apart from his medical skill, the Assistant Surgeon was very useful in the office because of his fluent Hindustani. He attended to any Indians on sick-parade, and there were usually some from the bowerjees (cooks) and bhistis (water-carriers) attached to the regiment.

It was now time to expect the arrival of the sick-parade. The water in the bowl on the Primus was brought to a boil. The M.O. and his staff rolled up their shirt-sleeves and washed their hands and fore-arms with a solution of carbolic.

"Put your head outside, Bombardier, and see what the omens for a quiet morning are," said the M.O.

The Bombardier stepped outside the tent-cover and took a look down the valley. He was horrified. A long, long trail of sick was coming up the side of the hill. He had never seen such an enormous sick-parade. They straggled along in twos and threes behind a sergeant who was himself a 'case.' But it was not the prospect of a full morning among the sand-sores that alarmed the Bombardier. The uncomfortable thought flashed through his mind that from the other side of the valley the sick-parade might easily be mistaken for infantry moving up to their positions for the coming attack. He only hoped that the Red Cross board would do its job.

He re-entered the office.

"Between eighty and ninety on their way up, sir," he reported.

"My word! . . ." exclaimed the M.O. "It must be curiosity to see our new quarters. You haven't been sparing with the sand-sore ointment I hope, Bombardier?"

The sick-parade clustered outside the office where slit trenches had been dug during the night by the Bombardier and the gunner orderly as a protection against spasmodic shelling. The sergeant in charge entered and handed the M.O. the sick report with the names of the men, their age, religion and length of service. The first patient was called in, a white driver from the Bombardier's own battery. He had developed a bad sore on the right shoulder.

" Good-morning," said the M.O. " What's your trouble ? Oh, one of those . . . Let me have a look. Oh, yes . . . I think we can fix that up all right. I'll have it dressed. Do you think you can carry on ? It isn't much, is it ? "

The Bombardier had heard the recitation so often that he knew it by heart. The M.O.'s verbal approach to sand-sore cases never varied by a single word. Occasionally, in a bad case, he decided at once that the man was not fit for duty and sent him back to échelon in the rear.

" Yes, sir, I can carry on," said the driver.

" Good . . . Go to the orderly. He'll dress it for you," the M.O. ordered, and marked the man's sick report 'I.A.T.' (Inflammation of the Ariola Tissue).

The Bombardier cleaned the wound by dabbing it with a pad of wool soaked in antiseptic lotion. Then he applied the magic ointment, and bandaged it up. He took the opportunity of gathering from the driver all the gossip of the battery. It was the only satisfaction he got out of sick-parade.

" Report in two days," he said when he had finished, two days being the length of time during which the ointment remained potent.

The driver departed and another sand-sore took his place. The Bombardier's spirits sank at the thought of all the others awaiting his attentions outside. A Section Officer from one of the batteries entered. He also was a sand-sore case. He was attended to by the Assistant Surgeon. The M.O. began to examine a youth of twenty who had just been returned to his battery by the base hospital as cured of shell-shock.

Suddenly there was heard the scream of a heavy shell outside. Immediately afterwards a violent explosion shook the office and caused the sand and earth to beat like a hail-storm upon the tent-cover over the entrance. The sick-parade, waiting in the open, scrambled into the slit trenches.

" That was a near one," said the Bombardier.

He had hardly spoken when two other shells dropped in the same place on the hill just behind them.

The shell-shocked youngster sprang from his seat in an

agony of terror. He started to run in crazy circles round the office screaming:

"I've got to get out of here . . . Let me out of here. . . ."

The M.O. caught him and gripped him firmly round the waist.

"Now don't you be a bloody fool," he said gently. "Nothing's going to hurt you. You're quite safe in here. Now sit down quietly and pull yourself together."

The soothing influence of his manner had its effect. The tortured youth allowed himself to be led to an upturned petrol tin near the wall, where he sat rigid, clutching his head in his hands.

While this was happening another three shells had exploded, this time in front of the office.

"I think they are bracketing on us, sir," said the Bombardier.

"It is getting a trifle uncomfortable," the M.O. agreed. "I'll just finish off the other case here and then we will clear the place."

Simultaneously, a shell burst right in the centre of the office. One single shell, the last to be fired.

The Bombardier heard no sound of explosion. He was only conscious of being violently lifted up in the air and hurled back again. All up his right side, from his ankle to his neck, he felt a burning sensation where the blast had struck him. Then blackness descended upon him.

He was the first of the occupants of the office to regain consciousness. He came back to himself with his ears singing, and half-choked with dust and fumes. Complete silence surrounded him. Not a movement of life. Dazed, he staggered to his feet and gazed through the subsiding fog upon the debris of the office as it was slowly made visible to him. The M.O. was lying with his feet on the table and his head on the floor, dying from a wound in the back of the skull. The Section Officer, with an end of the half-finished bandage still hanging from the sand-sore on his forearm, was stretched on the ground, dead, with one of the wicker-work medical panniers on top of him. The Assistant Surgeon sat upright against the wall, unconscious ; and close by lay the sergeant with a wound in the leg. The gunner orderly came-to while the Bombardier was completing his survey.

" Bloody hell," he groaned. " What was that ? . . . My ankle's broken."

" So is my right arm," said the Bombardier, weakly. He stumbled across to the entrance of the wrecked office.

" You fellows there," he shouted to the men who were still taking cover in the slit trenches. " Don't you think it's time you came and gave us a hand ? . . ."

At the same time he was nearly knocked over by somebody rushing past him from behind. It was the shell-shock case. He had been uninjured by the explosion and now, having regained consciousness, he dashed down the hill-side screaming in terror. The Bombardier slipped his broken arm in his shirt and started off in pursuit. But after running a short distance he had to give it up. He became aware that besides the broken arm he had been wounded in the chest by a shell splinter.

Weak and faint he returned to the remains of the office. Much to his joy, the Assistant Surgeon was showing signs of life.

" Are you all right, sir ? " he asked.

" Is that you, Bombardier ? " replied the Assistant Surgeon, in his quiet, grave voice. " Where are we ? . . . I can't see anything."

" We're in the office, sir. Or what's left of it. Got a direct hit."

The Assistant Surgeon seemed to be trying to force himself to understand.

" I wish you'd tell the M.O. I'd like to see him when he has a moment," he said, after some seconds' silence. " I'd like him to have a look at my eyes. I think I have been blinded by sand."

He raised his hands to his forehead and pressed the palms against his eyeballs in an effort to relieve the pain.

" I'm very sorry to say the M.O. is badly hit, sir," replied the Bombardier. " Very badly indeed."

" You mean he is dead ? "

" Yes, sir."

Another long pause ensued. The Assistant Surgeon still remained motionless with his back pressed to the wall, and his hands over his eyes.

"What about the others?" he asked, at length.

The Bombardier gave him an account of the casualties.

"Terrible . . . Terrible . . ." groaned the Assistant Surgeon. "And all my fault . . ."

"I don't see that, sir."

"Yes, my fault entirely. I ought not to have shifted the office. If we'd stayed where we were it wouldn't have happened," said the Assistant Surgeon in tones of bitter self-reproach.

The sergeant, whose leg wound was not very serious, had collected half a dozen men from the sick parade and set them to clearing away the debris. He had also sent back to the wagon-lines for a lorry.

"I'd better go to R.H.Q. at once and report," said the Bombardier.

"You get on the lorry with the others and go to the first field-dressing station," the sergeant replied, firmly. "I'll make the report."

The gunner orderly with the smashed ankle, the Bombardier, and the Assistant Surgeon were helped down the hill to the lorry. They travelled for some distance over the bumpy road to the nearest field dressing-station without a word being spoken. At last the Bombardier heard the Assistant Surgeon utter a deep sigh that almost became a stifled sob.

"Are you in pain, sir?" he asked.

"Nothing to the misery I'm in," replied the Assistant Surgeon sadly. "I've a load on my conscience. When I think of the M.O. dead, and all the others . . . I'm to blame for it. But for me this would never have happened . . . My fault entirely."

Moved by a profound pity for the mental sufferings of his companion the Bombardier did the first thing that occurred to him to alleviate them.

"I don't think you've anything to blame yourself for, sir," he said. "I might just as well blame myself. It is my firm belief that it's bad luck to kill a tarantula. And only ten minutes before we started digging-out the new office a fellow killed one practically on top of me. I said at the time I didn't thank him for it. And sure enough, look what's happened."

The Assistant Surgeon seemed not to be listening. He pursued his train of sombre reflections in a quiet, level tone, as if speaking to himself:

"I suppose I shall never see anything again . . . Never see a human face again . . . Not a single face . . ."

The Bombardier did not require telling that the one face which the Assistant Surgeon had in mind was a face he had never yet seen, the face of his infant daughter waiting for him in Cairo.

The lorry continued to bump them along the rough track.

"What is written is written," murmured the Assistant Surgeon, after a prolonged silence.

The Bombardier had no more to say.

V—Casualty in the Desert

"Home again," exclaimed the young Bombardier joyously.

Really, his home was two thousand miles away, in a turning off Mare Street, Hackney. And he hadn't seen it for years. But he spoke the words with an utter absence of irony. To the young and buoyant, 'Home' can assume the most unexpected of disguises, according to circumstances. It, may, for instance, assume the aspect of a desolate stretch of desert frowned upon by the bare grey rocks of an escarpment, and pin-pointed, as it was, on the Bombardier's map near the Salt Lakes in the Bir Hakeim area some fifty miles south-west of Tobruk.

"Home again! . . ." It was the Bombardier's invariable observation whenever they went into leaguer after a sortie. He loved the sensation—comparative tranquillity succeeding the concentrated excitement of the sudden attack on the enemy. First the dash forward miles into the trackless desert. The fog of swirling dust-clouds. The thunder of guns. The confusion of battle. Everything chaotic, seething, uncertain. Fortune in the balance. Victory . . . Tanks burning like red-hot cinders through the subsiding smoke of conflict. The mauled enemy sullenly withdrawing. And then leaguer where, till the next sortie, you dwelt in a world that seemed to have recovered something of its normal stability. A static bit of world for a change. A real oasis of the soul in the desert, where a man might, as it were, pick up again his personal bearings after having been whirled right out of himself, after having become more or less a stranger to himself. The contrast was swift and violent. And it appealed enormously to the temperament of the young Bombardier.

On this particular occasion his habitual satisfaction at going into leaguer was coloured by the knowledge that the latest sortie had been an unqualified success. In the middle of the hot May afternoon the mixed columns of tanks, 25-pounders and lorried infantry had struck off from leaguer just under the cliffs of the escarpment to the north of El Adem. An escort Troop of four 6-pounder anti-tank guns, each mounted on the back of a 3-ton Chevrolet, protected the flanks. The young Bombardier was No. 1 of the leading 6-pounder on the left flank. Only a week before his sergeant had been killed in action, and he was now looking forward to getting his step up. To this end, in addition to his natural qualifications, he had his friend Sergeant Turpin, Number One of No. 3 gun, working hard on his behalf with the Troop Commander. The Bombardier and the Sergeant were lifelong friends. Born in the same Hackney street they had gone to school together, enlisted together, served in the same battery in India, and ever since the outbreak of War had shared one another's gritty and thirsty fortunes in the Libyan desert. As a further tie they had chosen to marry sisters. Both considered that the elevation of the Bombardier to the dignity of a third stripe was the one thing necessary to set the seal upon their natural affinity.

For a time the column travelled due west from El Adem, and then turned south into the desert towards the Bir Hakeim area. After going about thirty miles they ran into a strong force of German Mark IV and Mark V tanks. The fighting was a mix-up, and lasted for some time. Not till eight in the evening did the battle simmer down. Then, leaving half a dozen of their number wrecked and burning along the low ridge, the remaining panzers drew off to the north-west. Highly pleased with its outing the column decided to go into close leaguer for the night in the open desert near the Salt Lakes. They travelled in snake formation and on reaching their destination formed up in a rough square. The tanks composed the outer sides, with all the soft-skinned vehicles and the 25-pounder battery in the centre. The four anti-tank guns sealed the rear. Being the last to pull-in, No. 1 gun, the Bombardier's, took position at the corner of the square facing the escarpment away to the left.

The gunners scarcely allowed the Chevrolet to come to a stop before they had jumped out and were racing towards the water-cart, each with a two-gallon can (captured from the Germans) in his hand. The young Bombardier descended more leisurely. The seductive influence of leaguer was already working its spell. He stretched himself luxuriously and surveyed the dark blue heavens lit by a moon, vivid stars, and some white Very lights going up from German positions a long way off. He listened to the howling of the desert dogs, content to know it would be to this familiar music he would fall asleep that night.

"Grand. Isn't it?" he exclaimed to the back of his driver.

"Bed-time story! . . ." was the driver's odd response, shouted in a voice loud enough for the next gun-crew to hear also.

From his seat in the Chevrolet the driver had been keeping an eye on the Troop Commander's 15-cwt. truck which had pulled up not far from the anti-tank guns. The Troop Commander had just returned from a visit to the Major at Battery Headquarters. He stood for a moment by the side of the truck and then raised his peaked cap vertically above the crown of his head, to the full length of his arm. This was the signal the driver had been on the look-out for. It indicated that the Troop Commander was desirous of the immediate presence of the four Numbers One of the Troop at the usual conference following a sortie. The Troop had nicknamed this conference " Bed-Time Story ".

" Get someone to lay my bed out on deck while I'm gone," ordered the Bombardier, meaning on the desert by the side of the truck. " And tell him to fold it so that I shan't roll out as I did last time. I'll have my Maconachie when I get back."

He hurried across to the Troop Commander's truck which bore the Divisional sign—a red desert rat—painted on the left-hand mudguard. The three sergeants from the other guns arrived simultaneously with him. The Troop Commander, a tallish, fair man, possessed a fresh rosy complexion that even the dust and heat of the desert had failed to scorch up. Attired in K.D. shorts, with a roll of maps under his arm, he took a seat on an empty petrol can, around which the others squatted themselves on the desert. The Troop Commander handed round cigarettes which they smoked furtively, concealing the glowing end carefully under the palm of the hand.

" How has it been going to-day, sir ?" inquired Sergeant Turpin, alluding to the general progress of the fighting.

" Not too bad," replied the Troop Commander.

He spread out one of the maps on the ground and explained, according to his latest information, the present state of the long-drawn out battle which was being waged against Rommel's armour in those fateful May days. A soft pool of light from his torch dappled the map as it flitted, moth-like, over the battle area. The quiet, conversational voice of the Troop Commander acquainting the men with the position of affairs in the various sectors, rather justified their nickname for the conference. It was soothing and comforting, even when the pool of light lingered for some time over one sector while the Troop Commander said :

" Here, I understand, the Jerry tanks have made some headway. Familiarise yourselves with the spot because it is important, though it is a good way from our area. But if they aren't stopped they may cut the Tobruk-El Gobi road. And that means that if we have to withdraw to the north-east we may run into something. The latest information received by the Major is that Jerry is five miles this side of that ridge in strength. But in a general mix-up like this, Heaven only knows where they may be now."

After lingering a sufficient period on the danger spot, the pool of light flitted to a new sector.

"Here we've dented their line a bit and done some useful damage," he continued in the same soothing bed-time voice.

So it went on till the Troop Sergeants had acquired a rough idea of the general progress of the widespread, fluid battle, and of the latest known dispositions of the enemy forces. None of them found the news, taken in bulk, very encouraging. They watched in a thoughtful silence the Troop Commander roll up his maps.

"Anyhow, we've had a very fair day ourselves," the Troop Commander remarked, cheerfully.

"Where are we going to-morrow, sir?" inquired the young Bombardier.

"You'll find out when to-morrow comes," laughed the Troop Commander. "Now what about the Troop," he proceeded "Any complaints? Anything wrong?"

Whereupon they settled down to discuss the domestic affairs of their own Troop, what new stores, equipment, and ammunition were, or soon would be, required. And more private matters concerning personnel. Now and again Sergeant Turpin took the opportunity of slipping in a word or two that he thought might enhance the Bombardier's chances of promotion with the Troop Commander. It was done very adroitly. But the Troop Commander, shielded by the darkness, smiled knowingly to himself.

All this took some time and the Bed-Time Story had lasted over an hour before the Troop Commander, rising from his petrol can with a yawn indicated that he had had enough. The men were just moving off to their respective guns when he said:

"Oh, I forgot to mention the bouquet. The Major is very pleased with us. We are the only Troop in the Battery that so far hasn't lost a gun. There's a bit to be proud of. Goodnight, everybody."

When the Bombardier returned to his gun he found his bed laid out 'on deck' beside the truck. His parting instructions had put the bed-making gunner on his mettle, and a bit over. Out of the blankets he had manufactured a very tolerable imitation of a scabbard. The Bombardier investigated and, being of slim dimensions, nodded approval.

As usual, the entire gun crew, hungry for news as only the desert can make a man hungry, clamoured round, burning with curiosity to know every word that had passed at the evening's conference. The Bombardier remained deaf to their appeals.

"Just you wait," he said. "You've had your supper, and I haven't had mine."

He was adamant. They stood by, curbing their impatience while he leisurely consumed his ration of Maconachie stew, eating it direct from the can, his own mess-tin being coated with a thick layer of unappetising grease from long-forgotten meals.

The last mouthful disappeared.

"Cough up," pleaded one of the gunners. "What did the fairy godmother tell you?"

"He said things were going pretty well," replied the Bombardier, carefully lighting a cigarette. "And he said we did a good job to-day."

"Well, we know that."

"And he said the Major is very pleased with us."

"Why?"

"We are the only Troop so far that hasn't lost a gun. Something to be proud of."

In the darkness one of the gunners shook himself uneasily.

"I wish he hadn't said that," he said gloomily.

"Why?" inquired the Bombardier.

"It's just the sort of thing that's like to put a jinx on us," the gunner answered, solemnly.

The Bombardier laughed scornfully.

"Neither the Major, nor anyone else, could put a jinx on you," he retorted. "You've had so many jinxes put on you since the push began that no new jinx could find lodging-room however hard he tried. You're just lousy with jinxes."

Quite unimpressed by the sarcasm the gunner commenced to expatiate upon the malevolent nature of jinxes in general, and the very small provocation they required to set their nefarious machinery in motion against the well-being of harmless and inoffensive soldiers. He illustrated his observations lavishly by references to past casualties in his own battery and others.

The Bombardier chucked his cigarette end away in disgust.

"Thanks," he said. "I've already had my bed-time story. I'm going for a stroll in the garden before I turn in."

He sauntered from his gun at the corner of the leaguer square towards the open desert. The moon had gone down but the stars burned more vivid than ever. It was so warm that although he was shirtless he felt well-clad. In front of him the desert stretched, dark and imponderable. And once more he enjoyed the idea of being in a stable, fixed world after the disintegrating flux of the sortie. How motionless, eternally stabilised everything seemed. You knew where you were. Just as he liked it. Nothing moving at all, except the two or three aeroplanes he could hear droning overhead. British, he assumed . . .

And at the same time he heard the whine of the falling bomb. He was just conscious of the subsequent explosion. Next moment he was landing upright on his feet with a terrific jar, a dozen yards from the spot where he had been standing. Dazed and choking with bomb-fumes he saw his Chevrolet a sheet of flame. More bomb explosions deafened his ears as the Messerschmitts unloaded methodically on the leaguer.

His right side, down to his foot, felt wet. He touched it and held his fingers close to his eyes. But even in the darkness he did not require to be told it was blood. From the top of his shoulder spread a blanket of numbness through which a nagging pain seemed striving to force its way. His right arm appeared to have become detached from his body, though he could still see it hanging down limply from the shoulder.

All this was the realisation of a few seconds. Then his attention returned again to the blazing lorry. Clearing the bomb-fumes from his throat he began shouting hoarsely to the gun crew.

"Joe! . . . Ginger! . . . Charley! . . . Jock! . . . Marty! . . ."

Nobody replied. He concluded they were all killed.

The leaguer, with bombs still dropping, was now in a state of utter confusion. All the tanks, lorries, and trucks were starting-up swiftly as possible in order to disperse into the open desert. The roar of engines, and the loud curses of drivers bewildered in the darkness, created a din which the falling bombs studded every now and then with their thunderclaps.

Suddenly the Bombardier remembered. Packed on the floor of the burning Chevrolet in between the trail of the gun was a box containing a hundred and eighteen rounds of ammunition. He turned away and began to stagger for safety into the desert.

After proceeding about fifty yards he heard someone running behind him. He stopped and in a second or two Sergeant Turpin stood before him. They stared at one another in silence, the Bombardier because he was still slightly dazed, the Sergeant because he was rendered speechless by the sight of the Bombardier's right arm, suspended from the shoulder, so it seemed, merely by a fragment of skin, and simply spouting blood.

"Harry! . . . My God, boy . . . What's happened to you?" he exclaimed at last.

It was the undeniable presence of a throb in his friend's voice and the glint of moisture in his eyes, that scared the Bombardier back into his cool resolute self for the first time since the explosion. Another second like this and he, too, might have tears in his eyes . . . So he shouted fiercely:

"Don't stand there laughing . . . Can't you do

something about it ? What has happened to the others ? I called out but didn't get any answer."

" Don't worry about them, Harry. They're all right," replied the Sergeant, back again to his natural steady voice, much to the Bombardier's relief.

The driver of the Chevrolet, uninjured, now emerged from the darkness, swore tersely at the sight of the Bombardier's injury and drew closer to investigate. The Sergeant pushed him roughly aside.

" Don't touch that arm . . . D'you want to pull it off, you bloody fool ? " he shouted frantically.

The Bombardier, dripping blood, laughed loudly.

" Better put a tourniquet on it," suggested the driver.

But the bomb-splinter had cut through the bone of the arm too near the shoulder. The Sergeant, terrified lest the dangling arm should suddenly drop off, made a sling from his trouser belt, passed it round the Bombardier's neck and gingerly lifted the arm into it. Then they tried to staunch the flow of blood with field-dressings. But the blood soaked through immediately.

" He'll bleed to death," said the driver.

" No, by God, he won't if I can help it," replied the Sergeant desperately. " You run back and fetch up my truck. And if you can't find mine bring up somebody else's. And move yourself. . . ."

The driver bolted back into the bombed leaguer, now a chaos of guns, tanks and lorries colliding in all directions with each other in their endeavours to make for safety. Bonfires of burning vehicles dotted the area, and the ammunition was exploding with an amazing variety of syncopated discord.

" Well, what are you going to do about it ? " demanded the Bombardier when the driver had departed. " Nothing ? "

Persevering in his effort to keep things on a normal plane he used the familiar provocative tone customary to his intercourse with his friend, though more pain was now seeping through the numbness of his arm and he felt his legs becoming slightly unsteady from loss of blood.

" I'm going to see you get medical attention," answered the Sergeant with vehemence.

" Where ? "

" I don't know."

" Fine bloody sergeant, you," laughed the Bombardier. The driver returned having retrieved the Troop Sergeant's own truck from the turmoil. The Bombardier insisted on being helped into the seat beside the driver's. He flatly refused to lie down in the truck behind. He was afraid he would never get up again if he did. But he kept his fears to himself.

The Sergeant jumped into the driving seat and the truck bounded forward into the blackness of the surrounding desert.

Not a word passed between the pair. To the Sergeant the event had outstripped speech. And the fact that he could feel some of the blood from his friend's right arm soaking through the left arm of his own shirt merely served to freeze whatever few words might have come to his lips. The Bombardier himself remained silent because he was trying to hoard the strength still left to him. He was now conscious of a definite ebb. Once or twice he felt on the verge of fainting away. But he was saved from this by a lucky chance. Right behind him in the truck was a fifty-gallon water drum, captured from the Germans in the previous day's sortie. A bomb splinter during the raid on the leaguer had cut a neat hole, six inches square, in the drum just behind the Bombardier's back. The contents were level with the bottom of the hole and, every now and then, when the truck bumped over a hummock of sand or heap of stones the water splashed out of the hole against the Bombardier's right shoulder, drenching his wound and reviving him like a shower-bath.

Meanwhile the Sergeant's mind was desperately endeavouring to visualise in all its details the map of the battle area which he had scanned during Bed-Time Story at the leaguer, and to recall each syllable the Troop Commander had uttered concerning the latest positions of the British and enemy forces. The problem besetting him was two-fold. How to get the Bombardier to a dressing-station without waste of a moment. And how to avoid driving straight into the arms of the enemy.

Around him he had the whole of the black trackless desert to choose from.

Quickly he made up his mind. He would strike north-east. True, the Troop Commander had said there was a possibility of the enemy tanks fanning out in that direction. On the other hand it was the line upon which he would be most likely to hit upon a British field-dressing station unless, of course, there had been a general withdrawal. So he drove north-east, steering by the stars.

For some miles they bumped blindly over the rough desert surface, once or twice narrowly missing a crash into some half-ruined sangar, whose low walls loomed up suddenly out of the darkness. On top of his errand the crushing immensity of the desert, crowned by the equally immense vault of the night, began to exert a depressing effect on the Sergeant. He developed the disagreeable sensation that he was the only living being in a world of vast solitudes. Simultaneously a dread seized him that he was driving with a dead man leaning against him. He slackened pace perceptibly.

"How are you feeling, Harry?" he asked, hoarsely.

And having ventured to put the question, now he was afraid lest the only answer would be a silence. But the Bombardier's voice responded as cheerily as ever.

"Fine, thanks. This drum's giving me a grand shower-bath. What are we stopping for? A drink?"

Out of sheer gratitude for the sound of that familiar bantering voice again the Sergeant sent the truck forward again with a terrific leap.

They covered another mile or two when, suddenly out of the darkness only a few yards from the bonnet of the truck a sharp challenge ripped the silence of the night.

"Halt! . . . Who goes there?"

The Sergeant pulled up with a jerk so unexpected that it send floods of water from the drum splashing all over the Bombardier.

"Friend . . . Got a wounded man . . ." he shouted back.

A couple of British infantrymen materialised out of the darkness, one on each side of the truck. Having satisfied themselves of the Sergeant's identity they directed him to drive straight on, another infantryman hanging on to the truck as a guide. He halted them a short distance from a depression in the desert where some infantry with several Bren-gun carriers were in leaguer.

"I'll take you over to the Major," said the guide. "Can your bloke walk?"

The Bombardier, in a weakish voice, answered for himself. Helped by the Sergeant and the infantryman he managed to remain on his feet till they arrived at the Major's H.Q.—a Bren-gun carrier a hundred yards away. The Major took one glance at the half-naked, blood-stained mess in front of him and shouted:

"Stretcher bearer . . ."

Immediately, an orderly, a lance-corporal, appeared, accompanied by two men bearing a stretcher, upon which the Bombardier was invited to lie down. This was beyond his powers. He could easily have fallen down in a heap. But no more. So he remained standing there with his knees gradually giving way, and eventually had to be helped on to the stretcher.

The lance-corporal knelt down and cut away the soaked bandage from the shattered arm.

"Oh! . . ." he ejaculated, drawing back at the sight of it.

The Major, who was watching, dived swiftly into the Bren-gun carrier. He reappeared next moment with a bottle of whisky, two-thirds full.

"Here, have a drink . . . a good one," he said holding the bottle to the Bombardier's lips.

By the time the Bombardier had relinquished the bottle he had become more conscious of what was going on around him. The Sergeant was giving the Major a description of the bombing of the leaguer. He spoke in forced undertones as though he were in a room with somebody dying. The medical orderly was trying to staunch the flow of blood from the Bombardier's arm, and pad the wound with large shell dressings. Watching the lance-corporal's changes of expression during this operation the Bombardier came to the conclusion that he was not finding it an easy job.

" How long can I go on bleeding like this ? " he asked.

" Don't worry. You'll be all right, old boy," replied the medical orderly, evasively.

" I asked you how long can I go on bleeding like this ? " repeated the Bombardier sternly.

The lance-corporal remained silent.

" Go on . . . You heard what he asked. Tell him the truth," exclaimed the Sergeant impatiently, after a pause. " I've known him all his life. He can stand up to the truth. It won't worry him. What he can't put up with is not knowing exactly where he stands. He likes things to be definite. Go on . . . Tell him . . ."

The medical orderly looked across to the Major for guidance. After a moment or two the Major nodded his head. There was a profound silence round the stretcher while they waited for the verdict.

" Six hours will be a lot . . ." said the orderly.

" Thanks," said the Bombardier, curtly. " What's the time now ? "

" Ten o'clock."

Miles away deep in the desert where lay the bombed leaguer, could still be seen the glow of burning vehicles, twinkling like a crop of fallen stars. The bombing had long since ceased, but every now and then they heard ammunition blowing up.

" You had better get back to your unit now, Sergeant," said the Major. " You've done all you can. We'll take care of him. You have begun by being very lucky. If you'd arrived five minutes later you wouldn't have found us. We are just packing up."

In the darkness the Sergeant bent over the stretcher. His bad moment had come. After the medical orderly's verdict he cherished no expectation of ever seeing his bosom friend alive again. This parting was for ever. . . . He did not attempt to check the tears that rushed to his eyes.

He gripped the Bombardier's left hand as if he never intended to let go of it.

" Good-bye, Harry . . . See you in Mare-street . . ." he forced himself to say.

" Good-bye, you old scrounger," replied the Bombardier.

" If we do happen to miss one another make it as easy as you can for the wife."

The Sergeant gave a brief nod, dropped the other's limp hand abruptly, and strode to his truck. Soon he was heading back across the desert for the blazing leaguer.

For the space of nearly half-a-minute the Bombardier remained motionless on the stretcher, his face fixed in the direction of the departing sergeant. Then, with a sudden movement, he jerked his head away and began to follow with a greedy attention, as if afraid of missing anything, the final preparations in the leaguer for departure. All he could see in the darkness of course, were those within a small radius of his stretcher. The medical orderly having at last done his best with the shell-dressings, covered him over with four blankets and offered him a drink from a water-bottle. The dispersed leaguer coagulated into two small columns, each headed by Bren-gun carriers. The lorried infantry formed up behind. The Bombardier's stretcher was carried to a 15-cwt. truck containing medical stores and equipment. It was too small to accommodate the stretcher, so the occupant was lifted off and deposited in the front seat next to the driver. The truck took up its position at the rear of one of the ' snakes '—the very last vehicle.

" Start up," shouted the Major. And they moved off.

Not a particle of activity, not an object, however small, that came within the range of the Bombardier's vision but received its moment or two of his concentrated attention. He allowed nothing to escape him, nothing he could see, hear, or smell.

Unforgettable in his mind echoed the words of the medical orderly :

" Six hours will be a lot . . ."

Six vital hours . . . Perhaps the last six hours of his life . . .

The Bombardier was not scared but he was desperately anxious to live out these six hours as fully as possible. Hence his grim and absorbing interest in everything around him, however trivial it might be. He dreaded missing a single moment of that six hours. He wanted to be fully conscious of each second. He did not even want to lose any of the precious time in thoughts of the past, or of his friends and relatives at home, even of Sergeant Turpin. All that portion of his life—the whole of it, so far—he had paid adieu to during the half-minute when he lay motionless on the stretcher in the leaguer watching the Sergeant swallowed up in the black cave of the desert night. Life to the Bombardier now had become matter of six short hours. That was all his could count on. He craved, with a craving that was almost morbid, to suck the very marrow from each instant.

Bumping along in the truck at the rear of the column his greatest fear was lest he should lose a fraction of the time left to him by fainting away, or even by lapsing into unconsciousness altogether. His senses oddly enough seemed to have sharpened themselves to his new needs, but as the effects of the copious draught of the Major's whisky began to wear off he was aware of a bodily weakness that increased. Besides, though his arm was slightly more comfortable after the medical orderly's attentions, he could still feel the blood spurting from the wound, soaking the blanket next his skin and making a sticky mess of the leg of his shorts.

The time passed. The Bombardier estimated that already a quarter of his vital six hours had been consumed, and the chance of salvation seemed as far off as ever. Inured to the difficulties of night driving across trackless desert he felt no impatience at the comparative slowness of their progress. They would arrive somewhere . . . sooner or later. And thinking it might be 'later,' he began to wonder how far ahead lay their destination.

"Where are we supposed to be heading for ?" he asked the orderly.

"I heard the Major say H.Q.," was the reply. "But I don't know which. It may be Brigade H.Q. If so, you'll be lucky. You'll get better medical attention there. How are you feeling ?"

"Still bleeding," said the Bombardier.

"I expected as much," the orderly observed, sapiently.

Shortly afterwards the two 'snakes' came to a halt about two hundred yards from a big leaguer. The Major drove on ahead in his truck and the Bombardier was lifted down on to a stretcher again. While he was being conveyed to the leaguer they met the Major returning, accompanied by an R.A.M.C. Captain.

"Ah, here's your patient, come to meet you," exclaimed the Major. "You're safe now, bombardier."

"Safe as the Rock of Gibraltar," said the Medical Officer, cheerily.

He stooped, pulled back the blankets on the stretcher, and in the light of his torch took a quick glance at the Bombardier's lacerated, blood-swamped arm.

"There doesn't seem much wrong with you," he observed. And the Bombardier willingly joined with him in a laugh at the ironic jest.

With eyes and ears missing not the slightest detail of the proceedings, the Bombardier on his stretcher was conveyed to an ambulance and slid on to the bottom bunk. Inside, when the door was closed, two bright lights were switched on. The Bombardier had been so long in the desert without seeing electric light that he felt he had undergone a novel experience. His eyes devoured the brown fittings and the medical equipment of the ambulance with the same hungry interest as ever. Except for a blanket-covered heap in the top bunk on the opposite side he was the only occupant of the ambulance. His feet now felt weighted with lead, and he found himself having to fight harder than ever against his increasing weakness.

Having donned a white jacket and laid out his surgical instruments the M.O. was ready for business. He drew back the blankets, revealing the Bombardier with blood covering his chest and soaking his shorts.

Immediately, the interior of the ambulance was filled with a hideous moan:

"Oh, God . . . Oh, God . . . Oh, God . . ."

The sight of the blood had started off the nerve-shattered occupant of the top bunk. He continued repeating the two words in a ghastly monotony as if wound up for ever.

"What's the matter with him? Bomb-happy?" queried the Bombardier.

"Yes. Don't let him worry you," replied the M.O.

" He's quite harmless . . . Now I'm just going to give you a shot of morphine to save you any pain."

He plunged the needle into the uninjured arm, waited a while, and then commenced to cut away the shell-dressing from the wound. Its nature brought a heavy frown to his forehead. The Bombardier, anxious to let nothing escape him, shifted his head and became absorbed in the spectacle of his life's blood being drained away from him.

Suddenly he received a sharp smack on the face—sharp enough to jerk his head in the other direction.

" You don't want to look at that," said the M.O. firmly.

He began to plug with dressings the holes in the wounded arm and the adjacent ribs, which had also suffered from bomb-splinters. This operation took some time. All the while the bomb-happy man in the top bunk continued to moan : " Oh, God . . . Oh, God . . ." Finally the M.O. wound the last bandage round the right shoulder.

" You'll be O.K. now for a while," he said, standing up. " We'll endeavour to get you through to hospital tonight . . . Meanwhile, try to get some sleep . . . If this chap on top will let you."

Sleep, however, was just what the Bombardier intended not to get, if he could avoid it. The little left to him of the six hours he had been allotted was far too dear to him. He felt himself weakening physically more and more, and this only increased his passion to extract all the interest he could out of whatever remnant of life remained to him. After the M.O.'s departure he tried to open a conversation with the bomb-happy case, but at his very first word the occupant of the upper bunk dived under the blanket and went dumb.

A medical orderly, a corporal, entered the ambulance.

" All O.K. ? " he inquired. " We're just starting."

" Where ? " asked the Bombardier.

" Tobruk."

" How long do you think it will take ? "

" Don't know. Likely as not we shan't get there at all. Jerry's all over the shop."

"Start up . . ." shouted a voice outside.

An officer took his seat in front beside the driver and the ambulance began its painful journey across the desert, bumping over the rough ground and almost heaving the Bombardier out of his berth whenever it bounced over a boulder in the darkness. A dimmed blue light shone in the interior, under which the orderly stationed himself and soon became absorbed in the task of deciphering a letter from home. No sound came from the bomb-happy case aloft. The Bombardier devoted himself to concentrating greedily on the minutest details of his surroundings but the dim light narrowed his scope and he felt, with irritation, that he was being cheated. So they progressed for some time in silence.

Suddenly the ambulance came to an abrupt halt, and showed no signs of proceeding again.

"What are we stopping for?" asked the Bombardier, impatiently.

"Enemy planes, I expect," replied the orderly. "If they see our shadow moving they're likely to come down and machine-gun us."

After a while the Bombardier could distinctly hear the drone of the planes overhead. The bomb-happy case also heard them and resumed his monotonous moaning: "Oh, God . . . Oh, God . . ."

"You're all right, old chap," said the orderly, soothingly. "Nothing's going to hurt you this time. They're some of ours."

The noise of the planes died away in the distance, and the ambulance jolted forward again. A few miles further on they entered a narrow wadi. They had not proceeded very far down it when they again stopped. This time there was no need for the Bombardier to ask the reason. Away to their front sounded the deep rumble of artillery fire and the explosions of shells.

"Don't look as though we're going through," remarked the orderly.

"What's the time?" asked the Bombardier.

"Couldn't say. My watch has got the gravel."

"Anywhere round about four o'clock, do you think?"

"Can't be far off . . . Why?"

"Because I'm in a hurry," said the Bombardier with a weak laugh.

"I know. The M.O. told us to get you through to Tobruk as quickly as possible. Wound still bleeding?"

"Quarts."

The gunfire ahead of them persisted. Finally the Bombardier heard the officer in front say to the driver:

"You wait here. I'll go forward and find out what is happening."

He was away for a long time. To the Bombardier, with the life-blood being drained from him minute by minute, the delay seemed interminable. At last even the orderly became restive. He opened the little window behind the driver.

"What's happened to him?" he complained. "Are we going to Tobruk? Or has he gone to Tobruk to bring the hospital to us?"

"Here he comes," said the driver.

The officer emerged from the darkness and climbed up into his seat.

"We can't proceed," he said briefly. "We'll go south into the desert. I've got fresh bearings."

The words fell upon the Bombardier's ears like a death sentence. He did not trouble to inquire of the orderly where their new destination might be. It no longer mattered. Wherever it was it would be too late to be of any use to him. He became more conscious than ever that the new bandages round his arm and shoulder were already saturated with blood. A great weariness descended upon him. He could no longer muster up strength to resist it. A last effort to concentrate on his surroundings flickered out. He closed his eyes.

The ambulance backed out of the wadi and commenced to jolt over the desert in a southerly direction. Mile after mile it bumped on while the Bombardier remained motionless, lying on his back, with his eyes still closed, resigned to his fate.

He was aroused from his lethargy by hearing the orderly exclaim: "Here we are . . ." He had not so much as noticed that the ambulance had again come to a halt.

"What's happened?" the Bombardier asked feebly.

"Main Dressing Station," said the orderly.

He quitted the ambulance, returning after a few minutes with another medical orderly. Between them they lifted the Bombardier on to a stretcher and conveyed him to a big marquee standing on the flat desert surrounded by several white tents. He was just conscious of being placed on the operating table, and of the shadowy figure of a doctor wearing a white coat over his khaki drill, bending over him, and administering an injection into his left arm.

"Do you feel very tired?" asked a voice that seemed very far away.

"Yes," the Bombardier murmured.

"Good. You'll go straight off to sleep now. Start counting and tell me how many you get up to."

The Bombardier counted up to four . . .

* * *

It was a fine sunny morning when the Bombardier returned to the world. It took him a little time to get his bearings, and then he discovered that he was lying on a stretcher in the shade outside one of the white tents of the Dressing Station. On each side of him were ranged other stretchers containing wounded. For a minute or so he lay wondering how he had come there. Then he remembered. And most vividly of all he remembered a scrap of conversation he had had in a past that seemed very far away.

"How long can I go on bleeding like this?"

"Six hours will be a lot. . . ."

He remembered how he had had to drag the information out of the reluctant medical orderly at the infantry leaguer. Six hours he had been given. Six hours from ten o'clock . . . Unless that bleeding stopped.

His mind took a sudden jump to his wound. He could feel himself comfortably bandaged up . . . Hardly any pain at all. Moreover the bandages were no longer soppy. Quite dry, they felt. It was the first time since the bomb splinter had hit him that he had not been conscious of the blood welling out of him. A thrill of intense relief ran through him.

He turned his head towards the occupant of the stretcher on his right.

"Got the time?" he asked.

The man glaned at his wrist-watch.

"Ten o'clock."

"Ten o'clock," repeated the Bombardier gaily. "That means I've been dead about six hours."

The other stared. He thought the Bombardier must have suddenly gone crazy.

VI—Overrun

THE BATTERY COMMANDER and his signaller, a bombardier, had just driven in from the Forward Observation Post on the right flank of the 25-pounders where they had been directing fire. Their khaki camouflaged armoured car, equipped with wireless mast, blue and white pennant flying, deposited them about sixty yards to the right flank of the right-hand gun of C-Troop. Cold, hungry, and thirsty they were well satisfied to be back at the position again. It was now past three o'clock in the November afternoon, the sky dull and overcast. A bitter wind blew from the north-west across the desert, so bitter that the gunners shivered in the pits although wearing greatcoats over their battle-dress.

For more than twenty-four hours the Battery Commander had been up at the forward O.P. They went there expecting to be back again long before nightfall. But events had befallen otherwise. They were pinned down to the O.P. throughout the night and till mid-afternoon of the next day. This wouldn't have mattered but for the fact that, not anticipating so long an absence, they had departed without taking sufficient rations to see them through. The Major's half-filled whisky flask had had to come to the assistance of the meagre water supply, and for the rest there had been a little bully beef, bully beef *au naturel* as it was out of the question to do any cooking at the O.P. On top of all, the night turned intensely cold. Therefore the Battery Commander, the signaller and their driver were in complete unanimity when a lull in the battle (so far as their sector was concerned) enabled them to close down and return to the comparative luxury of something warm to eat and drink.

As soon as the car pulled up the Major, a short tubby man with a round face and a quick blue eye, clambered from the turret, followed by the other two.

" Cook whatever you can find to eat," he said. " Have we got any tea left ? "

" Enough for one brew, sir," replied the bombardier.

" Good . . . I'm going across to the Command Post for a few moments."

It was the fourth day of the fierce and fluctuating battle that had developed in the area of Sidi Resegh as a consequence of the British drive to relieve Tobruk at the beginning of the second big Libyan offensive. It was a battle in which fortunes changed almost hourly. Rommel had flung the whole might of his panzer divisions into the struggle, and a tremendous tank duel was in progress over miles and miles of the empty desert, with the combatants bobbing up in most unexpected places, so that it was impossible to be sure at any moment from which direction an attack might come. This was the case with the 25-pounder battery which was attached to the 7th Motor Brigade Support Group. According to the way the battle moved, so the battery hopped around within the area of a two-mile square. At the present moment its guns faced a low ridge stretching almost along the whole of the sky-line at a distance of about two thousand yards from the positions. Behind this ridge, it was understood, lay the main forces of the Germans.

The four guns of C-Troop, mounted on their circular platforms twenty yards from one another, formed a rough arc. Before them as far as the foot of the ridge, and beyond, nothing met the eye but the drab waste of stony and sandy desert, broken here and there by small patches of low scrub. Thirty or so yards behind the guns was the

Troop Command Post, an eight-ton truck, fitted with a nine-foot wireless aerial and flying blue and white pennants, one above the other, the day's signal for British vehicles in battle. The four towing 'quads,' a couple of ammunition lorries, a signals truck with a spare wireless set, and other vehicles were dispersed in the wagon-lines, two hundred yards away, and safeguarded as much as possible from air attack by camouflage nets and scrub. The rest was the illimitable desert, flat except for small heaps of stones and sand hummocks, and looking very dirty and colourless under the overcast sky.

From the recesses of the desert echoed the noise of the disorderly, fragmentary battle which was still going on all around. To the north-west the gunfire was especially heavy and prolonged, and here a big tank clash seemed to have arisen. Elsewhere the firing was more spasmodic. A few bursts and then a silence. Occasionally these bursts sounded well to the rear of the battery area. It all added to the general uncertainty. No one had any clear idea of what was happening, or where. In the battery itself C-Troop, on the right, was enjoying a welcome spell of rest after a long morning's firing. The gunners, wrapped in greatcoats, lay around the gunpits, chatting, smoking and sleeping. One man remained on each gun, keeping his eyes skinned. By way of contrast, A-Troop, on the extreme left, had suddenly come into action again, and was engaged in some desultory shelling of a target behind the distant ridge. That was the way of it. Things flared up almost at a moment's notice, and died down almost as quickly. It was a battle in which anything might happen anywhere, and at any time.

The Major departed to the Command Post. The Bombardier lit a fire in the lee of the armoured car and started to cook some bully beef and three tinned sausages in a frying pan contrived from the bottom of a petrol tin. The driver boiled the water for tea. He filled a petrol tin cut in half with dry sand impregnated with petrol and applied a match. On top he placed another tin containing water, first having thrown in a bit of wood to prevent it from becoming 'smoked.'

" Water's boiling," he announced after a few minutes.

The Bombardier produced from the rations box in the car their most cherished possession, a little browned-stained muslin bag, filled with tea-leaves which had already seen long and faithful service. This he dropped into the boiling water and dangled it there on the end of a string for exactly two minutes.

" Better give it another minute this time," said the driver. " It hasn't dirtied the water yet . . . hardly. That ration's played out."

Nevertheless the Bombardier fished the bag out when the two minutes elapsed and began to squeeze it dry.

" I'm not taking any chances," he said. " We won't be extravagant till we're sure of the next ration. If necessary we might get another brew out of this, though it won't be anything to speak of."

" Nor to taste of," replied the driver gloomily. " The Major won't think much of this one, let alone the next. P'raps it will look more like tea when I empty the milk in."

The Bombardier squeezed the last two or three drops from the sodden bag and then deposited it again in the wooden rations box. Had it been some priceless treasure he could not have handled it with more tender care.

" Numbers One to the Command Post . . ."

In response to the Gun Position Officer's shout the four sergeants hastened from the gunpits to receive the latest information from the Major about the situation in their sector.

" That means we'll have to keep his food hot," the Bombardier said. " He won't be back for awhile."

" If he's wise he'll scrounge a mug of Command Post tea," the driver remarked.

They settled down to their share of the bully beef and sausages. Shortly afterwards the Sergeant-major strolled over to discuss the ration question, which was getting acute.

" What sort of a time did you have at the O.P. ? " he asked.

" Cold," replied the Bombardier, shortly.

" It was cold here, too."

"And hungry?"

"It would have been, but for a bit of luck," said the Sergeant-major. "D-Troop Commander captured a Jerry lorry, an officers' Mess complete with drink. They shared it out. So for the last twenty-four hours we've been living on Jerry tinned ham, soda-bread, and Munich beer. A very nice change."

The Bombardier, with bitter memories of the O.P. still fresh in his mind, nodded coldly.

"Very nice hearing about it, too," he said, ironically.

"I've kept a bottle of the beer for you over at the battery position," the Sergeant-major continued.

"That's a bit better," said the Bombardier, softening towards him. "Have a cup of tea?"

They sat round the small fire smoking and chatting. After a while the Bombardier, happening to glance in the direction of the wagon-lines, noticed a heavy tank coming towards them, a hundred and fifty yards away.

"What's one of our tanks doing behind there?" he remarked, casually.

Neither of the other two troubled to turn his head.

"Where do you expect to see it? Coming in front of the guns?" said the driver, derisively.

They carried on with their conversation. The tank continued to come grating up. It was only thirty yards away when the Bombardier took another glance at it. This time he noticed it was equipped with a run of small bogey-wheels at the top of the track.

"It must be a Mark III we've captured," he thought.

It was a thought that vanished as soon as it came. In its place he felt his heart give a decided thump against his ribs. There, just below the turret of the tank, he saw the unmistakable black cross on a white background.

"By God! . . . A Jerry tank . . ." he cried.

The Sergeant-major took one swift look, sprang to his feet, and roared: "Tank Alert! . . ."

In the gun-pits the resting gunners rushed to their positions. The Numbers One raced back from the Command Post. They all looked to their front, naturally expecting to see their targets coming from the direction of the ridge. But they saw nothing at all to begin with.

The intruder, without having fired a round so far, continued to lumber on between the armoured car and the gun on the right flank and then unexpectedly swung left on a course that took it right across the front of the gun positions. Immediately the Numbers One roared their orders. A few seconds later the right flank gun fired, and missed. The layer of the next gun had had time to lay on a small bush standing in the path of the tank. He coolly waited till the tank reached the bush. Then he fired. The shell, a H.E.119 with a cap on, for delayed action, hit the tank just below the turret. It stopped dead. Thin wisps of smoke began to curl out. A red glow appeared in the interior. In no time the tank was in flames.

Meanwhile another Mark III had appeared from the rear of the Troop position and was driving straight forward between the two guns on the left flank. Upright in the turret of this tank, head and shoulders projecting, stood a German officer, wearing a crash helmet and goggles. He had armed himself with a tommy-gun and busied himself spraying the pits to keep the gunners low. Whenever anyone tried to crawl from gun to limber to procure a rifle he was rewarded by a burst that sent him back to cover in a hurry.

From the turret of the armoured car at the other side of the Troop position the Bombardier took pot-shots at the officer with a rifle, and occasionally he, too, was a recipient of tommy-gun fire, too wild to do any harm.

Without interruption the tank drove steadily on through the positions at a speed of fifteen miles an hour. The goggled officer in the turret completely dominated the situation for the time being. Quite apart from the fact that no one dared stir without receiving the attentions of the tommy-gun, the 25-pounders themselves had no chance of opening fire on the tank till it had got past the gun shields. So the gunners flattened themselves beneath the trails and the limbers, and waited patiently while the bullets whipped up the sand around them. At last, having proceeded about two hundred yards farther, the tank drew clear of the gun shields. As though fully realising this fact, the officer redoubled his efforts with the tommy-gun. He poured burst after burst in the direction of the gun-pits in the vain hope of still keeping them quiet. A shell screaming a yard above the tank informed him that he might as well give it up. He took the hint. Head and shoulders hurriedly vanished inside the turret. A second gun opened fire. Soon shells were dropping all round the tank. But it seemed to bear a charmed life. It managed to travel almost half-way towards the distant ridge before it was hit, and even then the damage was not sufficient to halt it. Soon afterwards it disappeared from sight behind some sand hummocks. Later on it emerged again, crippled but creeping over the summit of the ridge : and the gunners gave it a final round or two, but without being able to stop it.

It was all over in five minutes. And in that five minutes a similar experience had befallen A-Troop and D-Troop away to the left. Four tanks had suddenly appeared from their rear and charged through the positions. Of this quartette, however, none managed to get away. The surprising five minutes ended with five out of the six tanks burning themselves out in the desert and the other just managing to crawl back home. As the three Troops had suffered no damage at all from the few shells the tanks had been able to fire, nor from the tommy-gun, this result was, from one point of view, quite satisfactory. But it was upon the crippled survivor rather than upon the five dead that the Major concentrated.

"If that was a mass reconnaissance, as I suspect," he said gravely, "it was worth their losing five to get one away with the news. Pity we let that one go. They've discovered our gun positions, and our gun strength. Well, it's no use crying . . . They must have blundered right into us without expecting it. It must have been as big a surprise for them as it was for us. I'm afraid, though, that the next surprise will be all on our side."

He hurried back from the Command Post to the armoured car.

"Call up the Troop Commanders to come to the car for orders," he said to the signaller.

The Bombardier switched the radio set to 'Send.'

"Hullo . . . Nine (the code number of the armoured

car) calling . . . Troop Commanders to report to armoured car . . ."

He switched to 'Receive' and waited. In a little while the replies followed one another.

"Three answering . . . O.K. . . . Off . . ." and so on.

"Message through, sir," he reported to the Major when all the Troops had answered.

Shortly afterwards the Troop Commanders drove up in their trucks.

"You all know what has happened," the Major addressed them. "We've been reconnoitred by the enemy, and unfortunately one tank got away. So they know all about us. We can expect a strong tank attack tomorrow. Column H.Q. has been informed what has happened. I haven't had word from them yet but I expect I shall hear something when I go over as usual tonight. Then I'll be able to tell you more. Meanwhile keep the guns in action. Don't limber-up and go into leaguer. But as soon as dusk falls bring up the quads and the ammo lorries to the rear of the guns so that we shall be ready for a quick move if the order comes."

The Troop Commanders departed. Just before dusk the Major drove off in the armoured car on his ten-mile cross-desert journey to Column H.Q. Around the gun-pits the men began cooking their evening meal, tea, bully-beef stew, and tinned potatoes. The excitement of the afternoon had worn off. The order that they were to stand-to throughout the night produced a somewhat sobering effect. By now they were fully acquainted with the opinions of the Major, and everyone saw in the smoking ruins of the tanks along their front not so much the evidence of a victory as a grim reminder that trouble was in store for them. The distant ridge loomed ominously in the fading light.

Column H.Q. was the Brigadier's car. When the Major arrived the time was nearly seven o'clock, the usual hour of the day's conference. He halted his vehicle a hundred yards from the Brigadier's and went forward on foot. Half a dozen other vehicles were similarly dispersed round the H.Q. They belonged to local commanders in the sector who had also come along to make reports and to receive orders for the next day.

The conference lasted longer than usual. The night was pitch-black by the time the Major returned to the armoured car.

" We shan't be going back tonight," he told the Bombardier. " It's too dark to travel safely. They're very worried at H.Q. about the reconnaissance. But it hasn't affected the orders. We carry on as usual tomorrow. Be ready to leave at dawn."

They bedded down for the night on the open desert beside the car. It was just beginning to get light when they awoke.

" Get in touch with the battery as quickly as possible," said the Major.

The Bombardier went inside the car and opened up the radio set.

" Hullo . . . Nine calling . . . Report my signals . . . Over . . ." he transmitted.

There was no reply. He tried again. Still no answer.

" What the devil is the matter with them ? " exclaimed the Major impatiently. " They can't have been attacked already or we should have heard the firing. Have another try."

Again there was no response from the battery. The Major began to show signs of uneasiness. Suddenly the Bombardier had an idea.

" I think I know what's wrong, sir," he said. " There was a heavy dew last night and I expect the aerial is all wet. We won't be able to get through till the sun comes up a bit and dries it."

" I hope you are right. Anyhow, we'll start back at once."

The mists of the night were already beginning to evaporate as the dawn strengthened. A red glow commenced to steal over the desert from the east in advance of the sunrise. After the car had proceeded half-way back to the battery the Major said :

" Call up the O.P.'s individually."

This time the Bombardier was successful in making contact.

"Anything to report?" he asked.

From each of the O.P.'s the reply was the same:

"Nothing to report."

"Thank God for that," said the Major heartily.

By the time they returned to the guns the men, hooded in their balaclava helmets, were cooking their breakfast. Around the gunpits the little fires burned with an orange glow in the pearly dawn. Two thousand yards in front of them the long ridge that hid the German strength was just emerging into outline as the sun showed its red rim over the eastern horizon. In a remarkably short space of time it was broad daylight. But the ridge showed no signs of activity. Evidently it was not to be a dawn attack as the Major had half-expected. The Forward O.P.'s were contacted again by the Bombardier, but still had nothing to report.

As on the previous day the armoured car pulled up on the outside flank of C-Troop, the first it came to, about a hundred yards from the end gun.

"We won't go to the O.P. to-day unless anything happens to either of the other O.P.'s," said the Major. "See if you can beg, borrow or steal any water so that we can all have a shave before the trouble begins. I don't mind if it's secondhand water. But not third-hand."

The Bombardier managed to scrounge half-a-mugful for which the Sergeant-major had no further use. They finished their shave, and their breakfast without any interruption on the part of the enemy. The calm continued, much to everyone's surprise. The Major spent most of the morning at the Troop Command Post where he was in wireless touch with the O.P.'s. The set in the armoured car closed down, giving the Bombardier a lazy time which he fully appreciated. The hours passed with scarcely any sound of firing, even from the more distant sectors of the battle. One of the 25-pounder Troops woke up things a little half-way through the morning by shelling some vehicles over the ridge. But it was only a ten-minute flutter. After that the desert lapsed into silence again.

"I'm beginning to think that tank didn't get home

after all," said the driver optimistically, as he and the Bombardier lay half-dozing a few yards from the armoured car.

" I'm not," replied the Bombardier without opening his eyes.

" Well, it's taking Jerry a long time to make up his mind. It must be getting on for one."

" I'm in no hurry," murmured the Bombardier, sleepily.

At that instant the tubby figure of the Major came running across to the car from the Command Post.

" Quick . . ." he cried. " Open up and get in touch with the O.P.'s. There's a flap on."

The Bombardier darted inside the car.

" Start up, and drive behind the guns," the Major continued to the driver. " Ten yards behind the pivot gun."

They followed the Bombardier into the car. As they moved off to the rear of the guns the Major stood up in the turret, sweeping the top of the far ridge with his binoculars. But so far there was nothing to be seen. The Bombardier began his circuit of the O.P.'s.

" Hullo Two . . . Nine calling . . . Give situation report. . . ."

The reply came back the instant he had switched over.

" Hullo Nine . . . Two answering . . . Situation report . . . General movement of enemy armoured vehicles. . . ."

There followed the map reference and compass bearing on which they were travelling.

The Major hurriedly scanned his map. It needed scarcely more than a glance to show him that from the bearing given the enemy tanks were driving direct for the battery position. By now the other O.P.'s had replied. All of them confirmed the first report.

Just as the armoured car pulled up behind the pivot gun of C-Troop a further message was received from D-Troop Command Post.

" Hullo Nine . . . Five calling . . . O.P. withdrawing under heavy enemy shell fire. . . ."

At the same time the guns of the two Troops on the

left of the position began to roar. They fired without ceasing and the desert echoed with their thunder. From behind the ridge the German 75 mm. guns came into action simultaneously. Shells screamed through the air, exploding all round the battery position in a very intensive barrage which everyone knew to be the preliminary to a tank assault.

Standing up in the turret of the armoured car, the Major called at the top of his voice:

" G.P.O., Numbers One, and Sergeant-major. . . ."

The six men named ran up and grouped themselves in a semi-circle round the turret. Still wearing merely a service cap, binoculars hanging from his neck, and map case in hand, the chubby-faced Major addressed them with the light of battle dancing in his blue eyes.

" We shall probably have a close tank attack very shortly," he said abruptly. " The method of dealing with it will be as follows . . . The gunners and every one near the positions will remain in slit trenches when the attack starts, and must wait till the tanks draw in. Impress that on all concerned. No gun must fire till the tanks have come in to a thousand yards . . . Any questions ? . . . Then, all right. . . ."

He had just finished when the whine of a 75 mm. shell sounded almost on top of them. The Major ducked inside the turret. He barely had time to get his head down before the explosion came. The car gave a violent shudder. There followed a rattle of splinters on the steel plates. Dust and fumes of cordite invaded the interior in a choking fog. Then all was quiet.

The Major thrust his head out of the turret.

" My God ! . . ." he exclaimed, horrified, and jumped to the ground.

The shell had landed a few yards from the side of the car where the group had been standing. The six of them were now stretched on the ground. At first the Major thought they were all dead. But a he was clambering from the turret the Sergeant-major and two of the sergeants staggered to their feet, dazed but unhurt except that the Sergeant-major had been slightly wounded in the arm by a shell splinter. The G.P.O. lay unconscious with a bad wound in the stomach. Both the other sergeants were dead.

The Major, rendered speechless for a moment by this sudden disaster, was recalled to the even grimmer realities of the situation by the voice of the Sergeant-major.

"Here they come, sir . . . Hundreds of them."

The Major rose to his feet from his examination of the G.P.O.'s wound and turned his binoculars upon the distant ridge. Scores of tanks were swarming over the sky-line towards them. He let his glasses drop.

"Tank Alert! . . ." he roared. "Gun Control . . ." which left each individual gun to fire at its own discretion and to pick its own targets.

"Carry the G.P.O. to the Command Post, and put on a field-dressing," he ordered the two sergeants who had by now partially recovered from their shock. "We can't do anything more at present. I'm very much afraid he is finished."

He hurried back into the armoured car, followed by the Sergeant-major.

"Open up your set and try to pick up any information you can," he said to the Bombardier.

The Bombardier opened up. But the frequency was jammed with messages. All he got was a confusion of sounds out of which he could make no sense.

"Air full of messages, sir . . . Can't get through," he reported to the Major after persisting for some time.

"Keep trying . . ." ordered the Major, once more thrusting his head out of the turret.

The Troop was now enduring a barrage that grew in intensity as the minutes passed. The bursting shells churned up the position into clouds of dust and earth. In addition the enemy began sending over armour-piercing shells that arrived with a high-pitched, ear-piercing whistle and ricochetted all over the place. So far the 25-pounders had remained silent. In accordance with the Major's orders, the gunners remained crouched in the slit trenches till the tanks should come within the thousand-yards limit.

Inside the armoured car, the Bombardier continued trying in vain to establish contact with the outside world. Two more shells burst near the car.

"Why don't you drop that bloody aerial," grumbled the driver. "It's of no use now. All it's doing is drawing their fire on us."

"I'm keeping it up," replied the Bombardier firmly. "If we get hit we get hit."

With his glasses fixed on the approaching tanks the Major at last decided that the moment had come.

"Take Post . . ." he shouted above the din.

The gunners scrambled from the trenches and ran to the battered gun-pits. After the previous order of "Gun Control" there was no need to wait for further commands. The four guns fired almost simultaneously. The noise of the salvo was deafening. The Major, who had not been expecting it quite so suddenly, ducked back into the car with the blood pouring from his ears.

"Are you hurt, sir?" inquired the Sergeant-major.

His query went unanswered. A shrill whistle bore down on them from outside. With a thud that seemed to lift the armoured car off the ground an armour-piercing shell hit it square on one side, went straight through and out the other. The Major, the Sergeant-major and the Bombardier were flung violently into a heap. When they disentangled themselves it was discovered that no one had been hurt save the Bombardier whose left leg was slightly burned by pieces of hot steel splinter. But the shell had smashed the wireless set and put it completely out of action.

"Lucky it didn't ricochet inside," commented the Major, grimly.

He pushed his head out of the turret again and withdrew it swiftly. A salvo of 75 mm. shells burst on the Troop position with a colossal uproar. The flying debris hammered against the sides of the car like bullets from a machine-gun, and the reek of cordite choked the air. As soon as the din subsided the Major took another look outside. Almost immediately he shouted back to those inside:

"Evacuate the car . . . Follow me to the guns. . . ."

He jumped from the turret. The Sergeant-major went next. As the driver was in a difficult seat to get out of quickly in case of emergency, the Bombardier said:

"You'd better go first."

But the driver refused to budge.

"I'm staying here," he said, obstinately. "I'll take my chance where I am. After that las shell I reckon this vehicle's got luck."

"All right. Have it as you want it," replied the Bombardier. "I'm going. . . ."

He jumped out and ran after th Major who, revolver in hand, and crouching as low as his tubby figure permitted, was racing towards No. 1 gun. The Bombardier had scarcely reached the gun-pit when he heard the scream of a couple of shells. He looked round in time to see both of them hit the armoured car. Almost immediately it became a mass of flames.

The Major paused for a moment or two outside the gun-pit to take stock of the situation. The salvo of seventy-fives had proved disastrous to the Troop. Only one gun, No. 2, remained in action, and that was being manned by three gunners. All the gun crews had suffered fatal casualties. The dead, dying, and the badly wounded were strewn around the trails and the limbers. One of the guns had been smashed by a direct hit. A shell had blown the Command Post to bits. Over the tragic scene of death and destruction hung a thick fog of dust and smoke. To the front the enemy tanks were steadily drawing nearer. A dozen of them lay wrecked or burning themselves out on the desert, but dozens more were rolling up and opening fire as they came within range. Seen through the haze of the battle their gun-flashes whipped out in tongues of blood-red flame.

"Come with me," shouted the Major to his two companions. "We'll get this gun going and knock out a few more."

The three of them stepped over the bodies in the gun-pit. The Major jumped into the layer's seat, to sight and fire the gun. The Sergeant-major traversed for him. The Bombardier prepared the ammunition and loaded. With the first round they hit a tank at four hundred yards.

As the tanks drew in, the artillery barrage ceased. No. 2 gun had run out of ammunition and the three gunners who had been manning it crawled into No. 1 gun-pit to lend a hand there. There was no sound of firing from anywhere else along the battery position. The Major concluded that the other Troop had been completely silenced by the barrage. A fierce anger seized him, and it was with the utmost satisfaction that he saw his next shell hit the nearest tank just below the turret.

At this juncture an unexpected newcomer crawled into the gun-pit. It was a begrimed and dusty runner from D-Troop. He brought news that the two othe Troops had withdrawn upon belated orders from Column H.Q., and that C-Troop was to bring up the rear.

" All right," replied the Major, curtly. " When I've finished what I'm doing."

A couple more tank shells burst just behind them. They were followed by a crack from the solitary 25-pounder, and once more the Major scored a hit, this time on a tank that had halted to rescue the crew of one that had already been knocked out.

" Load . . ." he shouted exultantly to the Bombardier.

The Bombardier was just pushing another shell into the breech when the rattle of machine-gun fire sounded to the rear of the pit. He glanced behind and distinguished the greyish-blue tin-hats of German infantry who had pushed forward under cover of a smoke screen.

" Infantry behind us, sir," he reported.

A second burst of fire emphasized his words and the bullets whizzed through the air and slapped against the back of the gun shield.

" Damn it . . . We can't fire any more," exclaimed the Major regretfully. " Take cover. . . ."

The occupants of the pit flattened themselves to the ground and crawled as far under the gun as they could get. Another fusillade came from the rear. In front the tanks had halted about two hundred yards away, but were still sending over an occasional shell. After a few seconds the Major raised his head and shoulders and took a quick look round.

" We can't stay here any longer," he said. " If we do we shall be in the bag."

He considered for a moment or two.

" Stop where you are," he ordered, and before his companions had time to realise it, he jumped up and started to run right across the front of the enemy infantry in the direction of the wagon-lines, two hundred yards away.

The others watched him in an amazed silence. Every second they expected to see him hit. Bullets flicked up the dust all round him and cut through his clothes. Once or twice the tubby little figure stumbled and they thought he was finished. But he recovered his footing and bounded on untouched until he reached the nearest vehicle in the wagon-lines, a 15-cwt truck.

"What's he going to do?" breathed one of the gunners.

"If I know anything of the Major he's going to come back for us," said the Sergeant-major with a queer laugh.

The Major found the driver taking cover under the vehicle.

"Get up and drive back to the position," he ordered. "Quick. . . ."

Too excited to speak, the watchers in the gun-pit saw the truck start up and move over the desert towards them, under fire all the time. They knew their fate was in the balance. The odds were heavy against them and their suspense grew more and more unbearable with every yard the vehicle covered. In the tension of those seconds they forgot the bullets singing round their heads, and could hardly refrain from standing up to get a better view of the Major's progress.

At last the truck was within twenty-five yards of them. They could see the Major standing up coolly in the passenger-seat, waving his left hand slowly in front of the driver as a signal to slacken speed a little, and motioning with his right hand to the occupants of the gun-pit to jump in at the back as he was going by.

"I'm not stopping," he yelled out. "Be ready. . . ."

They were ready all right! As the car drove past the six men, including the runner, darted from the gun-pit and clambered up behind, which was not too easy to do in the circumstances for the truck was piled high with kit.

"Everybody on?" asked the Major.

"Yes, sir."

"Then go like hell! . . ."

The driver turned the way he had come, accelerated, and they drove off at top speed through the wagon-lines in the direction to where the Major expected the Column had withdrawn.

"Good show while it lasted," he said, reminiscently after they had travelled for a while in silence. "But we are out of it now," he added.

"Sounds as if he was sorry," muttered the Sergeant-major to the Bombardier.

And so it did.

VII—Battery in a Hurry.

THE battery of eight 3.7 inch A.A. guns had been in action defending the airfields in the desert south of Sidi Barrani ever since the start of the big push, a month before. What with the days when the dust came up, and the days when the water-cart didn't, the gunners found it very dry work indeed. However, it gave them something to write home about. One of the layers had set the standard.

"I have been saving up my water," he wrote to his wife, "filtering it, even the drops I use for shaving. On Friday, Jimmy and I had saved two whole pints and we decided to make it a washing-day. We washed ourselves, then our shirts, then our socks. What was left we cut into blocks and buried in the sand. . . ."

All the Battery agreed that for purposes of home consumption this struck exactly the right note. They took it as the model for their own private correspondence. And some artists even attempted embellishments. Nevertheless, behind all these flights of fancy their privations stuck out real enough.

When, therefore, towards the end of December, orders came for the Battery to move forward to become part of the defences of the port of Tobruk, which had just been relieved after a long and bitter tank battle, great was the jubilation. Garrison water might have its drawbacks, but to the thirsty gunners it was nectar by comparison with 'desert water,' which as often as not meant no water at all. Tobruk also set the optimists again canvassing the possibilities of a Christmas dinner (a dream that had almost vanished) though few were bold enough to suggest of what the dinner might consist. The more sober spirits contented themselves with the assurance of many a delicious swim in the Mediterranean.

The convoy, consisting of the eight guns, and the lorries laden with ammunition, spare gun barrels, and stores, moved off on December 23rd. For the first day and night they struck straight across the rough desert on a compass bearing which, on Christmas Eve, brought them to Sidi Resegh where they picked their way through the litter of wrecked tanks, burned vehicles, abandoned guns, and fly-smothered corpses left behind by the great battle of the previous week. Soon afterward the convoy leader sighted the road ahead. It was the road constructed by the Germans during the long siege to circumvent the perimeter of Tobruk. Although a poor thing by British standards the convoy hailed its smooth hard surface with relief after their rough and bumpy journey over the desert. One gun had broken down when almost in sight of the road, its carriage fractured by continuous bouncing on the rocky surface of the ground. It was left behind for repair. A couple of hours later the remainder of the convoy rolled over the last ridge, and Tobruk—the promised land flowing with garrison water—lay beneath them.

"It's as good as a drink already," observed the driver of the leading gun tow-er to the sergeant beside him. "Looks a perfect picture."

And so it did, after the pictures they had been used to in the desert. From the top of the ridge the cluster of white houses showed no signs of the battering they had received, from British and enemy bombers alike, ever since the desert war began in earnest, twelve months before. They grouped themselves in a cool and pleasantly composed fringe with the blue Mediterranean sparkling in the sunshine behind. Only the harbour, where the wrecks of fully fifty vessels, ranging from cruisers to supply craft, were visible above the waters, provided the scene with a grimmer note.

Anticipating that they would be able to make good use of Tobruk in the near future, even if the Christmas dinner failed to materialise, the Battery halted on the plateau of the ridge to await the Major who had gone ahead into the town to arrange about gun sites. When the Major's truck drove up shortly afterwards, he jumped out like a man possessed of a sense of urgency.

"Don't unpack," he ordered. "We are moving on immediately. We are to proceed to Benghazi without delay."

It was undeniably a shock, even to those who had limited their expectations to a swim in the sea. As for a Christmas dinner. . . . Beneath the ridge the cool-looking white town, with its promise of garrison water, mocked them like a desert mirage. Benghazi non-stop. . . . That meant days of doubtful rations, and no real rest.

"But we haven't captured Derna yet, sir," said the Battery Captain, in surprise.

"Yes we have," replied the Major. "This morning."

"Still, Derna isn't Benghazi."

"Our tanks will be in Benghazi before we get there, however much we hurry," the Major assured him. "And we are in a hell of a hurry from now on. The Navy have signalled they will want heavy A.A. protection round Benghazi harbour before they can start unloading supplies. So we haven't any time to waste."

The spell of Tobruk was broken. The Battery shaped itself for its new task. Lorries were speedily despatched to the nearest petrol supply point to get fuel for the four hundred mile dash across Cyrenaica. Others went in search of what extra rations they could collect.

"We move off in two hours," said the Major tersely. "Get what you can, and go without the rest."

What they managed to get was hardly enough to go round. Each vehicle received a fair share with the warning to make it last as long as possible.

Precisely at the end of the two hours, the guns bumped down the shell-blasted road leading from the ridge towards the harbour and on to Windy Corner, ill-famed as the hottest spot in any air raid. Here they turned left and away up the hill, past the A.A. Gun Operations Room on the right, past the static 3.7 inch pits on the left, past the prisoners of war cage, full of new occupants from the broken German and Italian divisions, and so on to the junction of the old Tobruk road and the new Axis road, some fifteen miles further on, known as Rommel's Way. Here stood the massive stone monument, erected by the engineers who had constructed the by-pass, in commemoration of their own feat, a monument now chipped and disfigured by machine-gun fire and shell splinters.

Throughout the dark night the convoy groped its way along the crater-pitted surface of Rommel's Way without a halt, save for a brief check-up after being spattered by machine-gun fire from a lone night fighter. A bleak dawn ushered in Christmas Day. It found the Battery grinding and bouncing along at a steady thirty miles an hour, despite some of the roughest roads in North Africa. In the lorries the gunners were tossed about in all directions. The going was so bad that conversation degenerated into a mere word or two jerked out here and there between the incessant bumps. Sleep was quite out of the question, although it was already over forty-eight hours since they had had their last at Sidi Barrani.

A third of the way down the convoy, in a 3-ton lorry, three gunners were having a particularly uncomfortable ride atop a load of boxed 3.7 inch ammunition. Suddenly, without warning, the back of the lorry filled with blinding smoke. The camouflage netting that draped the vehicle had somehow or other wound itself round and round the propeller shaft and caught fire. The gunners yelled at the top of their voices to warn the driver, but the lorry was travelling so fast that the noise of the engine drowned their shouts. They hammered on the back. Still the driver could not hear. He drove on completely oblivious of the volcano he was sitting on while the smoke grew thicker and thicker round the ammunition boxes. Eventually, in desperation, one of the gunners clambered out on top of the tarpaulin cover of the vehicle and crawled forward to the roof of the driver's cab, a precarious little trip during which he was more than once nearly pitched off by the violent jolting.

This time the driver heard the noise overhead. He stuck his head out of the open window to discover what was the matter. Clouds of smoke pouring from the rear of the vehicle met his gaze. It took him a fraction of a second to sum up the situation.

" Hold tight! . . ." he yelled, giving a mighty twist to the wheel.

The lorry took a leap off the road and stopped dead. The gunner on top was flung off on to the desert, but scrambled to his feet unhurt. The other two gunners jumped out, followed by the driver. By now the lorry was ablaze. It was only a matter of seconds before the flames would reach the ammunition. The four men raced as fast as their legs would carry them to the shelter of a ditch, a hundred yards away. They dived into it just as the first rounds began to explode.

The ammunition cases were packed tightly together in the lorry, and the shells flew up into the air at all angles. Behind, the driver of the vehicle following had pulled up a hundred and fifty yards away when the explosions started. In less than a minute the Major dashed up in his truck.

" Who told you to halt? " he demanded angrily. " You are holding up the whole convoy."

" It doesn't look safe, sir," the driver ventured to remark, and in confirmation of his words another couple of shells exploded almost simultaneously.

" Safe! . . ." echoed the Major. " Damn it, we have no time to be safe."

He raced up the road, made a swift reconnaissance of the blazing and exploding wreck, and drove back.

" Start up," he ordered, " There's ample room to get by. Put on as much speed as possible. And don't swerve off the road as you pass. The edges may be mined."

All the gunners dismounted and clung to the off-side of the lorry, holding on as best they could. In front the explosions had now reached the dimensions of a miniature barrage. Crouching low in his seat, the driver sent his vehicle tearing down the road at top speed towards the fireworks. The rest of the convoy followed suit. By amazing good fortune they all passed through the ordeal without any casualties. Shell splinters cut holes in the canvas of some of the vehicles and peppered two or three of the drivers' cabins. But that was all.

Late in the afternoon the head of the convoy rounded the last bend in the mountain road above Derna. And the gunners drew astonished breaths. "How the hell are we going to get down there?" everyone began to ask. At first glance it looked a tough problem. There lay the little white town, a sheer two-thousand feet below them. But the Italian engineers had made quite a good job of the narrow road which wound and twisted round the steep mountainous slopes likes a gigantic serpent writhing in torment. The Battery began a crawling descent down the narrow pass. As several of the tortuous bends had been mined by the retreating Germans their progress was not without its extra hazards. The leading lorries had the worst of it. They had to go forward cautiously, testing the ground to see if it would stand the weight of the heavy guns.

It was a relief to all concerned when the convoy began to draw clear of the pass. But they were destined not to emerge unscathed. Having successfully negotiated the dangers on the ground, the blow fell on them from the air. Just as the tail of the convoy was winding round the last loop, three Ju. 88's, roaring over the mountain top, dived with ear-shattering screams upon the vehicles crowded in the pass, undeterred by the vigorous machine-gun fire from the gunners. There was nothing to do but to speed up and hope for the best. For a minute or two bombs burst on each side of the pass and the valley echoed the roar of the explosions. Rocks and stones hurtled through the air. Under the wheels of the lorries the road trembled with the concussion. The last bomb of all dropped plumb on the back of an ammunition lorry. There was a terrific flash and a deafening explosion. The lorry and its crew were blown to pieces.

When the planes had departed the convoy was halted for a few minutes. But there were no survivors. Nothing, indeed, left even to bury. While the Major and the Battery

Captain were checking-up, the gunners in the waiting lorries seized the opportunity to make tea. Like all Desert Rats they had become expert in the art of 'Brewing up' on the move. As soon as a lorry halted out jumped the No. 1 of the 'Brew-up' team, shovel in hand, and scooped a shallow trench in the desert. Into this he flung a small incendiary block taken from a captured Italian mine. Meanwhile No. 2 of the team had collected in an old petrol can whatever water there was available, and placed it over the trench. No. 3 threw in a match and the incendiary block blazed into a fierce flame. Two minutes sufficed to boil the water—unless the can melted first, a tragedy that had been known to happen more than once. No. 2 pitched in the tea, the sugar and the canned milk. One hundred and fifty seconds from stop to start—and a couple of gallons of boiling desert tea.

So it was now. A score of incendiary blocks flared by the roadside, and a score of petrol cans bubbled and steamed on top of them. The halt was brief but sufficient. "Mount! . . ." came the order, and the convoy rolled on to Derna.

There they learned that the British had already entered Benghazi. The news made the Major more impatient than ever to push on.

"Crack on every ounce of speed you can," he ordered. "We are keeping the Navy waiting. Stop for nothing."

Then he drove off ahead to Benghazi to arrange about the gun sites, leaving the convoy to be brought along by the Battery Captain.

Throughout a pitch-black and drizzly night they forged on. At noon on Boxing Day they entered Barce, prettily situated in one of the few fertile plains of Cyrenaica. Barce had been badly bombed and shelled. Houses were shattered, streets blocked with debris, and crossed overhead with sagging wires from wrecked telephone and telegraph installations. One unfortunate gunner, standing up in the back of his lorry to stretch his legs failed to duck in time as they passed beneath a tangle of wiring. A drooping wire caught him under the chin and neatly whisked him out of the lorry—and out of the world too. Despite the frantic efforts of his companions to drag him back, he fell into the road under the gun behind. A few minutes and no more were all that could be spared. The Battery sped on, leaving him in a hurriedly-dug grave by the roadside.

By nightfall the convoy was heading for the mountains separating the plain from the coast. Again it was pitch-black and drizzling with rain. The men were weary, cold and hungry, for the rations were by now running low. It became a nightmare of a journey, trying to keep up a speed in the solid darkness over strange roads whose surfaces had been rendered slippery as glass by the rain, and which were, in addition, littered with the wreckage of the retreating German and Italian armies. One 3-ton lorry skidded and overturned in a ditch. Shortly afterwards, while turning a bend, a gun skidded and broke its towing-arm. It had to be abandoned for the time being, thus reducing the strength of the Battery from its original eight to six guns. At last, despite the fact that the Navy was waiting, the Battery Captain decided that further progress was too risky under the conditions. A halt was called for the odd hour or two of darkness left before the dawn. It was the first stop of more than a few minutes that the Battery had made since leaving Tobruk on Christmas Eve, three days before. The drivers simply dropped over the wheels exhausted, and fell fast asleep.

When light came and the convoy moved on once more the Battery Captain had every reason to be satisfied at his decision. Rounding the first bend in the road the leading gun found itself confronted by an enormous bomb-crater into which it would inevitably have plunged had they continued for another fifty yards in the darkness.

Now they entered upon the last lap. Benghazi, with the Navy waiting, lay only some sixty miles away. But before reaching their goal they had first to cross the mountain range in front. This meant negotiating the Tocra pass, by far the most formidable stretch they had yet encountered. As the morning advanced the convoy climbed laboriously up and up miles of winding road until it finally reached the old ruinous fort which marked the top of the pass. From here the road made a sudden break to the right and then plunged steeply down the other side of the mountain, executing an amazing succession of hairpin bends with, in many places, one-in-four gradients. That in itself would have been bad enough. But rounding the turn at the top of the pass the leading gun found that a stretch of road, built on the side of a precipitous slope, had been completely blown out of existence. Nothing was left except precipice.

The convoy halted. Accompanied by the Motor Transport Officer, the Battery Captain went forward to reconnoitre the problem. Eventually they discovered indications of a narrow, disused, mud track leading steeply down the mountain side and hitting the road, almost at right angles, a hundred yards beyond the demolition.

" I see nothing else for it," observed the Battery Captain after a few minutes uncomfortable consideration. " We'll have to bring the guns across the mountain and drop them on to the road below via the track. Can we do it ? "

The M.T. officer screwed up his face in pain at the prospect.

" At first glance I should say ' Impossible '," he said. " But I've seen the Impossible done so often during the campaign that it's hardly worth saying."

" Quite right," retorted the Battery Captain. " It isn't. The cold facts are, we have got to get to Benghazi, and there's no other way for us but down that track. We've got to take all the risks."

" If we can build up a reliable gripping surface on the mud surface we may stand a chance," the M.T. officer said dubiously. " It will have to be good enough to keep the vehicles from sliding down to the road and over the precipice before the drivers can pull 'em round the bend. It's the guns I'm most concerned about. That's a one-in-five slope. A ten-ton gun gathering momentum down it isn't going to be easy to swing on to that narrow road. A near-miss won't be any good here. There's a five-hundred feet drop waiting the other side."

"Better not think about it," remarked the Battery Captain, quietly. "We'll get the track built up, and see."

Soon the order was being shouted back along the line of lorries: "Every man out and up at the front except machine gunners and air sentries." The whole Battery was put to the task of giving the muddy, slippery mountain track a holding surface, with stones and jagged pieces of rock, down to its junction with the road. It took a considerable time, but at last the Battery Captain was satisfied that nothing more could be done.

"It's up to the drivers now," he said finally to the M.T. officer.

He called the drivers of the G.T.V.'s together and addressed them briefly.

"It's a ticklish job in front of you," he said, "but there is nothing else for it. I can't advise you how to tackle the business. It's up to each man to use his wits to cope with whatever trouble arises. But I hope there won't be any. We've given the track a good surface, and it should grip. The main thing is, keep cool. And if you do start to slide, take it with a rush. If you once get out of control you'll be lost. Go down in convoy order, No. 1 gun first, and one man on the gun-brake on each limber. That's all . . . And good luck."

The M.T. officer, a young subaltern, had elected to be first to make the test. He had furnished himself with quite a tricky load—a 3-ton truck towing another broken down 3-tonner which in its turn, towed an old trailer. With the entire Battery grouped around as spectators he took the wheel of the leading truck and bounded down the newly-made track, almost recklessly so it seemed to the onlookers, who had expected him to creep down cautiously. But his tactics justified themselves. Just as he appeared about to career over the precipice he swung round his wheel. The leading truck took the sharp swerve safely on to the road and its speed gave the vehicles in tow no chance of dragging themselves, and their leader, over the edge. The M.T. officer pulled up fifty yards further on. He dismounted, his face damp with sweat which he was honest enough not to attribute entirely to the mere physical exertion of the descent.

Encouraged by his success the drivers of the other transport vehicles—the 3-tonners, 15-cwts., and the like—took the slope confidently, and all managed to attain the road beyond the gap without mishap. But this was only the overture. Everyone understood that the real drama would begin when it came to the turn of the guns. By the time the first gun-towing vehicle was ready for the descent quite an impressive hush had embraced the whole Battery. Instinctively it was recognised that this was no fit moment for the usual display of back-chat and facetious advice. In silent groups the gunners clustered on the mountain side wondering what would happen. The Battery Captain felt his load of responsibility double itself in weight. Only a brief time before he had advised the M.T. officer not to dwell upon the 500-feet drop that, on the other side of the road, awaited the unlucky driver. But now he found it very difficult to banish the thought, even for a moment, from his own mind. The drivers of the G.T.V.'s were, he knew, all first-rate men. He had the utmost confidence in their skill and courage. That was something to be thankful for. But he had to take into account the fact that they were very weary men, worn out by the strain of being at the wheel with scarcely a break since they left Sidi Barrani five days before. He couldn't disguise from himself that in the job before them they needed something more than skill and courage.

"I only pray the first has th luck to get through all right," he said to himself. "It will make all the difference to the others."

The huge gun-towing vehicle, dragging behind it the ten-ton gun, lumbered over the mountain side to the head of the steep track. The descent began. And almost immediately the Battery received a shock. The combined weight of the G.T.V. and the gun proved so great that, although the brakes held the wheels firmly locked, gun and tractor started to slide irresistibly down the track like an avalanche, gathering momentum as it went.

"My God! She's going over . . ." cried the No. 1 of the gun.

And it was the single thought that possessed the entire Battery as, with a fascinated horror, they watched the great mass sliding down towards the precipice.

But the driver, an experienced heavy transport driver before the war, knew exactly what to do in the emergency. Despite the risk of going clean over the edge, he eased off his brakes to enable the wheels to regain their grip and give him some steering control. By the time he reached the vital junction of track and road he had acquired considerable speed. It still looked odds on his going over the brink. But at the crucial moment he swiftly pulled round his wheel. The strain on man and vehicle was terrific; so great that at one point the near-side wheels of the G.T.V. quitted the ground for several yards. The Battery gasped. It was touch-and-go. Then they found relief to their feelings in a hearty cheer as the driver drew out safely and neatly parked his gun by the roadside some distance down the pass.

The next driver had a much less sensational trip. He proceeded cautiously and his gun managed to maintain its grip on the surface all the way down the precarious slope. He was never in the slightest danger of going over, and took the sharp bend on to the road at the bottom with no more fuss than turning a street-corner. The Battery Captain began to breathe more freely.

The third gun started down the slope. Immediately things began to go wrong. Before it had travelled half-way the G.T.V.'s wheels lost their grip and, as the brakes still held, the vehicle slewed round.

"Look out! . . . She's twisting," yelled the M.T. officer at the top of his voice.

Whether the driver could hear him or not didn't matter. The warning came too late. The huge G.T.V. swung round into a position practically at right angles to the ten-ton gun behind it. On the gun itself a desperate gunner wrenched with all his might at the wheel which applied the gun brakes. It made no difference. The weight of the gun pressed down on the lorry, and a second avalanche began to traverse the steep slope towards the precipice. Suddenly, with a sharp crack, the metal bar by which the gun was towed snapped off at the hook.

The breaking of the towing-arm temporarily gave the gun a few feet of clearance from the G.T.V. in front. It was only a matter of a yard at the most. But in that small space the momentum gained by the gun was considerable. With a loud smack the limber of the gun hit the lorry broadside, and the Battery gasped in horror as, under the impact, gun and vehicle in one combined mass, rolled down the slope towards destruction.

To the helpless onlookers it seemed that nothing could prevent the disaster. And nothing human did. Gun and consort pursued their uncontrolled course down the track. They swept across the narrow road. They crashed through the slender concrete posts that marked the edge of the precipice. And there, with the 500-feet drop directly below them, they stopped. Just a matter of a few inches . . . Just one of those unaccountable freaks of fortune. . . .

It took the spellbound Battery some seconds to realise what had happened. Then, as one man, they rushed forward to hang on to the gun and lorry, fearful lest the dreadful movement should start again though, to be sure, they would have been quite powerless to do anything if it had. The air was filled with shouts and a confusion of orders and suggestions.

"Pull the bloody thing back. . . ."

"Chock the wheels. . . ."

"Winch it away from the edge. . . ."

"Keep clear of the side of the road, everybody. It may collapse and send us all over. . . ."

Finally, out of the confusion emerged a plan of action. Ropes were lashed round the gun. Boulders were placed under the wheels lest it should slide forward again. The gunners took the strain, some on the ropes, some on the gun itself. With difficulty and much exertion the ten-ton gun was manhandled out of danger back on to the solid road. The lorry, released from the crushing weight, was soon hauled into safety.

The Battery Captain remounted the slope with mixed feelings. His satisfaction that complete disaster had been averted was considerably tempered by the unpleasant fact that, nevertheless, he was minus another gun. Without its towing axle it could not be moved. It would have to be left by the roadside and recovered later. Since the Major had quitted the Battery outside Barce to push on in advance to Benghazi, this was the second gun they had had to abandon. And there still remained three more whose chances of joining the casualties were, the Battery Captain was forced to admit, by no means remote. Under the disquieting influence of such thoughts he set the gunners to work again repairing the surface of the track which had become deeply rutted and slippery from the passage of the first three guns. The men packed it as tight as possible with bits of jagged rock and arge stones, and finally the Battery Captain decided it was safe to proceed with the business.

The fourth gun behaved itself perfectly. The driver descended slowly and steadily on to the road below as though towing a ten-ton gun down a one-in-five gradient leading straight to a five-hundred feet drop were mere child's play. It came as a most welcome relief after the sensations o the previous descent and the Battery Captain's spirits rose accordingly. He hoped the worst was over.

His hopes were soon swiftly shattered. The fifth gun had hardly proceeded ten yards when it began to get out of control. Its progress developed into one long skid that nothing would stop. With wheels locked, and the driver desperately trying to check the descent, gun and vehicle slid down the track, charged across the road at the bottom, hung precariously for a second or two over the precipice and then, as the road edge crumbled beneath the weight, plunged out of sight.

It all happened so swiftly that the gunners could scarcely believe their eyes. They rushed in a body to the edge of the road and, looking over, saw the gun and vehicle in an inextricable heap five-hundred feet below, not far from where the lower road wound round the mountain side. A score or more scrambled down the side of the precipice and ran to the wreck. They were amazed to find the driver alive, though half-unconscious. And not only alive, but unhurt. The gunner on the limber was not so fortunate. He was dead, crushed beneath the weight of the ammunition boxes and the spare gun barrel.

Meanwhile the remainder of the Battery were again busy repairing the treacherous track. The Battery Captain with impassive face, gave them no time to brood on the disaster. Especially he was concerned about its effect on the driver whose turn was yet to come. He walked over and had a word with him, and was relieved to find that the tragedy did not appear to have shaken the man's confidence that he could manage the descent without any trouble.

And so, in fact, it proved. The sixth and last gun went down the slope at a steady pace, never out of control, took the sharp bend at the bottom beautifully, and parked itself at the tail of the convoy lower down the road.

"Mount . . ." ordered the Battery Captain, immediately.

Now that the ordeal was over he was anxious to get away from the damned spot as quickly as possible. Already several valuable hours had been lost. It had been a tragic business. But he could not blame himself. His orders had been to go right through to Benghazi without delay. And he had carried them out in the only way possible. A tough proposition. . . . On the whole, perhaps he could consider himself lucky that he had only lost two guns. . . . Grand fellows, those G.T.V. drivers. . . . Especially the last man, in face of what had just happened. . . .

The convoy sped down the pass, making child's play of the hair-pin bends of the winding road after their ordeal higher up. A sudden twist in the road brought them close to the wreck of the ill-fated gun. The Battery Captain considered that, despite their hurry, a few minutes halt was justified. He went across with a burial party, saw the dead gunner decently interred, and pin-pointed the position of the grave on his map for the use thereafter of the Graves Registration Unit.

Night was falling when the weary, depleted Battery approached Benghazi, and were met by the Major in his truck with the gun sites marked on his map. In the darkness they lumbered through the deserted and bomb-wrecked streets. Weary as they were after being bumped and bounced about in lorries over rough roads for so many days and nights their time for rest had not yet come. The guns had to be brought into action, the ammunition laid out and fused, the instruments set-up and lined-up, the dials checked. Every minute counted. Beyond the harbour the Navy was waiting.

The Battery was still in a hurry. . . .

VIII—Forward Observation Post

For a week or more the 25-pounder battery had been roving around in the Bir Hakeim area, about forty miles south of Tobruk, shooting up enemy concentrations. It had been free and easy, enjoyable work, here today and gone tomorrow, according to the sway of fortunes in the prolonged and desperate battle which, during that June, the retreating Eighth Army was fighting against Rommel's Afrika Korps, a battle destined to provide the enemy with an open door into Egypt which did not close until it was slammed fast against them at Alamein.

During some of the bitterest fighting the Free French Force operating in the desert on the left flank of the British suffered severely from dive-bombers, and were constantly under shell-fire from German 75's, 88's, and 105's. In an attempt to relieve the pressure on them a small column, consisting of the 25-pounder battery and a company of infantry with Bren-guns and carriers, was despatched south from Bir El Gobi. Orders were simple :—to take on enemy batteries wherever they could be found, and to knock them out. It was the sort of commission that suited the adventurous disposition of the Battery Commander down to the ground. He took full advantage of his freedom of action. The little column became as mobile as an armed reconnaissance. No sooner was one target dealt with than the guns hooked-in and were away after another. The Troops did all their firing from open positions in the desert, never digging-in lest they might have to move in a hurry. At nightfall they went into close leaguer, with the Bren-guns and the infantry dispersed round them.

Finally, they pushed up a few miles north of Bir Hakeim, and it was here they made their prime discovery—a big concentration of enemy tanks, guns, and armoured cars, simply asking to be harassed, as the Battery Commander gleefully put it. He went forward in a Bren-gun carrier accompanied by a signaller to scout round for a good O.P. for himself; and the Troop Commanders did likewise. A low sandy ridge overlooked the enemy leaguer, fifteen hundred yards away, and the Major eventually decided on a spot near the centre where a little cover was afforded by some patches of scrub. The two Troop O.P.'s were established on his left and right flanks respectively.

So as to minimise the chances of being spotted the Major moved in just before dawn, accompanied by an infantry subaltern in a second Bren-gun carrier for local protection. The two carriers crept over the desert, ascended the ridge in the darkness, and parked themselves tightly side by side in the belt of scrub. The occupants spent the brief time that still remained before dawn in tearing up scrub and completely camouflaging the exterior of the vehicles.

"Get all the exercise you can," said the Major, cheerfully. "It will be some hours before we have any more. Once light comes we shall be pinned down to the cars. No getting out to stretch your legs. What's more, be careful not to make any sudden movements in the car, in case of being spotted. I warn you because, when the sun gets really going, we shall find it pretty hot and sticky, cramped up inside, and are bound to grow restless."

The pink glow of sunrise began to tinge the drab face of the desert.

"That's our signal," said the Major.

He took his place in the front of his carrier next to

the driver. At the back sat the signaller with his wireless set. The subaltern, his driver, and Bren-gunner likewise ensconced themselves in their temporary prison alongside the Major's. And so they waited till the light should become strong enough to illumine the secrets of the desert. As the minutes passed the Major began to experience a slight anxiety lest daybreak should reveal an empty scene before them. Might not the concentration have moved-off somewhere in the darkness? It was quite possible, so quick were the changes in this fast-moving battle. If so, he thought, he would regret the loss of such a grand target till the end of his days.

Therefore, it was with unconcealed joy that, as the sun rose, his eyes feasted upon the enemy leaguer situated just as it had been when he first reconnoitred it the evening before.

"Very appetising, isn't it?" he called to the subaltern.

And from the point of view of a Forward Observation Officer of a battery of slick 25-pounders, it indeed was. Nothing was missing. There were tanks, guns in positions, armoured cars, hundreds of soft-skinned vehicles, and lorried infantry, all dispersed over a fairly wide and deep area, but most of it within range of his guns. He studied it with the appreciation that an art connoisseur might bestow upon some particularly interesting canvas. Through his binoculars he could plainly discern parties of men cooking meals, and other parties sitting around eating.

"My one fear is that we shan't be allowed to stay here long enough to do a really fat and juicy job," he said to the subaltern, letting his glasses drop. "I like this O.P. We'll never find anything nearly as good on the ridge if they shell us out of here."

Then he settled down to the business on hand. His first shells had barely landed in the concentration before they were joined by a couple of others directed by the Troop Commanders from the O.P.'s on his flanks. At first the enemy did not appear to pay much attention. They seemed to regard it as a bit of desultory shelling that would die down in due course. But when, later in the morning, something like a salvo dropped among the soft-skinned vehicles and set half-a-dozen of them ablaze, the observers on the ridge detected a new stir of activity below.

" Damn it. They're breaking leaguer," exclaimed the Major, in deep disgust. " And we've hardly hurt them."

The subaltern laughed.

" Unkind of them not to stay and be shot at, I must say," he said. " I'm only surprised they haven't moved before. Or started to smoke us out."

" Yes . . . There they go," continued the Major sadly, watching through his glasses the concentration as it moved out of range.

Tanks, armoured cars and lorries crawled away over the desert and gradually faded out of sight. The Major sent a few ineffective shells after them.

" Looks as though we are not going to get any more shooting," the subaltern remarked.

" It certainly does," agreed the Major. " But I think we'll stay up here for a bit longer," he added. " It's a very nice O.P."

" I'll go so far to say it was," laughed the subaltern. " Are you expecting them to return ? "

" Well, I admit I have a hope. Faint, but nevertheless. . . ."

" Why ? "

" I've a sort of idea at the back of my mind that, for some reason or other, it is rather important for that little bunch down there to remain where we first found them. In which case there is a chance of their coming back."

" What makes you think so ? "

" Of course you've noticed that track proceeding from the leaguer which runs right across our front and disappears behind that elbow-ridge on our right."

" Yes."

" Did you notice anything particular about it ? "

" It seemed pretty busy."

" Exactly. And busy with what ? All the morning those fast little open German staff cars have been continually running backwards and forwards along that track. Sometimes as many as three officers in a car.

They disappear behind the bend of the ridge, returning in half an hour or so. It has been going on all the time. I don't know what you think about it but I'm willing to have a big bet that there is some Jerry H.Q. round that bend."

"I wouldn't bet against you," said the subaltern.

"Well, that's why I'm staying on here for a bit," continued the Major. "Just to see if my hunch is right. A big concentration like that, with what is evidently an important H.Q. attached, is where it is—or was—for some special purpose. It won't want to be shifted too readily."

"How long do you intend giving them ? "

"I'm willing to let them have two, say three, hours to put in an appearance again," replied the Major generously.

He ordered the signaller to get into touch with the other O.P.'s and told them to hang on till further notice.

An hour passed and the plain in front of the ridge remained as empty as before. Another half-hour passed. Suddenly the subaltern, sweeping the horizon with his glasses exclaimed :

"Dust going up, sir."

The Major raised his binoculars with alacrity. He saw it, too, straight ahead of them, the unmistakable sign of vehicles on the move over the desert. The dust drew nearer. Watching it attentively, the two officers shortly afterwards distinguished half-a-dozen tanks and some armoured cars emerge from the low cloud.

"I've won," exclaimed the Major, exultantly. "They've come back. Now we can proceed with the business."

The concentration settled down practically in the old position, but this time the soft-skinned vehicles were not so much in evidence. Once more the 25-pounder shells began to hot things up.

A little while afterwards a staff car containing two German officers sped swiftly down the track which led from the leaguer to behind the elbow ridge.

"They've started again," called the Major to his companion. "It's an H.Q. . . . I'll bet my boots."

At the same time the boom of a coupl of 88-mm. guns

echoed over the desert, and their shells began to burst on the top of the ridge.

" Jerry evidently has made up his mind that we are to be the ones to shift next time," said the Major. " It'll be a nuisance if they find us and we have to quit this spot. Any change will be for the worse. Besides the waste of time."

Shells continued to drop fairly thickly on the ridge, but practically all in the direction of the two O.P.'s on the Major's flanks. The Troop Commanders, he guessed, were having a hot time. He was not very surprised when he received a message from Don-Troop Commander:

" Hullo Nine . . . Five calling . . . Leaving present position . . . Heavy shell fire. . . ."

A similar message arrived soon afterwards from the other O.P. And so it went on. The O.P.'s on the flanks were constantly having to withdraw and find new positions, which were plastered by shells as soon as they began to operate. Meanwhile, the Major remained undiscovered. Not a shell fell anywhere near them. The Germans had evidently concluded that there were two O.P.'s on the ridge, and no more, and devoted their attention to chasing these around. The Major didn't complain. It left him undisturbed to harass the concentration at his leisure.

The morning wore on. Inside the two Bren-gun carriers the occupants sat cramped and stiff, and sweltering under a fiery sun that beat down upon them from a brazen desert sky. There was hardly a breath of air. The mere effort entailed in resisting the temptation to get some relief from the broiling heat by a change of position in their seats seemed to send up the temperature, and stimulated beads of sweat round their eyebrows and lips upon which thirsty and stinging flies settled in droves. Yet they dared not make any but the slightest and most cautious movement for fear of betraying their presence, and sharing the fate of the other two O.P.'s. The steel plates of the carriers grew hotter and hotter. The air became stifling. But there was nothing the occupants could do about it, except to stay put and be grilled.

The hours passed painfully and slowly without any incident to enliven them beyond the ordinary routine of the shelling. Occasionally the concentration grew restive and moved away a bit, but it soon returned again after shelling the ridge vigorously. It was now getting well on into the afternoon.

"Look . . . There goes another," called the Major to the subaltern.

"I see," was the brief reply.

Another German staff car had detached itself from the concentration and was speeding down the track leading towards the invisible H.Q. So it had gone on at intervals throughout the day. And as time passed, the Major's interest in these activities became deeper and deeper. So sure as a car appeared on the track he was certain to call his companion's attention to the fact. The infantry subaltern, stewing in the heat, began to grow faintly bored. He found it monotonous enough, stuck up there in the O.P. with nothing to do but shake the flies off his face, without being subjected to the additional monotony of the Major's notification of the appearance of every separate staff car. The only variation was: "Here it comes back," when a car returned. And that also became monotonous. He could not imagine why the Major should continue to display such a lively concern in the dodging about of a few staff cars, which were impossible targets for him, anyhow. The subaltern would have been much less bored if he could have had an inkling as to the end to which the Major's interest in staff cars was unconsciously shaping itself. But that was something even the Major himself didn't realise as yet.

Towards the end of the afternoon came a diversion. A new target presented itself. A big tank commenced to crawl slowly down the track from the leaguer.

"It'll be a pin-point target for the Troop, but I'm going to try to hit it," the Major called to the subaltern, who welcomed the change.

"C-Troop . . . Take Post. . . ."

The signaller despatched the order to the guns.

"Through, sir," he announced in a second or two.

"Zero . . . Two-three-O degrees . . ." ordered the Major, having obtained the rough angle off the map with his compass and protractor scale.

From the distant Troop position the order was repeated back in verification.

" Five thousand . . . Range . . ." continued the Major.

From the other end came the request :

" Check method of fire . . ."

" No. 1 ranging . . ." replied the Major.

In a few moments the signaller in the Bren-gun carrier got the repeat back from the Troop position.

" Fire . . ." ordered the Major.

" Shot one, sir," announced the signaller on receiving the intimation from the guns. Both the Major and the subaltern raised their glasses and looked-in.

The shell screamed over the ridge and they saw it drop barely twenty yards in front of the tank.

" Good round to start off with," commented the infantry officer.

" Less Ten degrees . . . Five thousand . . ." ordered the Major, this also being the automatic order to fire.

" Shot one, sir," announced the signaller.

Looking-in this time they could see that they had not achieved a direct hit. But the explosion appeared to have put the tracks out of action, for the tank came to a standstill.

" I've stopped him. But I haven't hit him hard enough yet," observed the Major. " I'll put down another round just to make sure."

" Repeat . . ." he ordered.

The third round burst on top of the tank.

" Excellent bit of work," said the subaltern, enthusiastically.

For a while they kept their glasses fastened on the tank. It remained motionless, dead.

" There's no sign of smoke, so we haven't set it alight," said the Major. " But it's out of action all right. No need to waste any gunfire on it. Yes, that last round was a beauty. . . ."

While they watched, a large vehicle drew away from the concentration and sped down the track towards the wrecked tank. As it passed broadside to the ridge the observers on top saw that it was an ambulance with a big Red Cross painted on the side. It pulled up beside the tank and a couple of men jumped out. One climbed into the turret. Two wounded men were handed out, placed in the ambulance, and driven back to the leaguer. The tank remained on the track, lifeless.

"I suppose the other chaps inside are dead, so they didn't bother to remove them," said the Major, letting his glasses dangle from his neck. "Well, that's finished with."

He dictated a message for the signaller to send back to C-Troop.

"Information regarding last target . . . Target, enemy tank moving along track . . . Now stopped disabled . . . Casualties . . . No. 1, rest. . . ."

"Message received . . . O.K. . . . Off," came the reply.

The Major resumed the routine harassing task that had been interrupted by the appearance of the tank. The enemy's reply to the incident was to shell the ridge once more with a vicious persistence. Again the two O.P.'s on the flanks reaped the benefit of the Major's success. They were driven to find new homes. But not a shell dropped anywhere near the O.P. that had caused the mischief.

In the middle of the roar of the German 88's another staff car sped from the leaguer down the track to the presumed H.Q. The Major, between looking-in at a couple of rounds, eyed it with contemplation. The accumulation of all the similar goings-on of the day was beginning to have its effect upon his natural taste for excitement. He began to realise what it was he had been hankering after for so long.

"You know, it's a great temptation," he called to the subaltern.

"What is?"

"I must confess it has got under my skin, watching those cars running about all day long with impunity. Right under our very noses. It's all too damn cheeky for my liking."

The subaltern pricked up his ears. There was something in the Major's tone that led him to suspect that the subject of German staff cars was no longer to be regarded as a bore.

" What do you propose doing about it ? " he asked.

" We've had a very pleasant day, except for the heat and the blasted flies," proceeded the Major calmly. " Quite a good day. But I really don't think we ought to go back without trying to winkle one of those officers. That would round off the day quite nicely. Besides, who knows ? We might get Rommel himself."

" And if we don't we will have had the sport," laughed the subaltern. " It's a grand idea. Tell me more."

" This is the plan as it presents itself to me," said the Major. " When the light begins to fade and we see another car leave the concentration we will start-up the engines and both dash at top speed down the ridge. If we can cut on to the track at the bottom before the car gets there we shall simply stop it and invite it to accompany us, with its contents, whatever they may be."

" That's short and simple enough, and seems pretty sound," the subaltern agreed. " If I may make a suggestion, though, I think it would be better if we didn't go down abreast, but if I kept a little to the rear so that I could cover you, if need be, with the Vickers."

" Yes, that's sense," replied the Major. " There's only one thing that may upset us. We shall be limited as regards time. The job must be done between sunset and the time it gets really dark. That doesn't give us very long. We shall have, say, three-quarters of an hour from the time the sun drops below the horizon. And if no car appears during that time well, it will be just too disappointing after all the traffic we've seen going backwards and forwards since morning."

A bit more shelling occupied their time till the sun began to sink in front of them. Already the desert behind, over which they had to travel back to the gun positions, was darkening rapidly. The two of them sat in the Bren-gun carriers intently watching the ball of the sun as it dropped lower and lower to the horizon. The Major glanced at his watch. It had gone half-past six. Shortly afterwards the sun's rim touched the distant desert line. In a remarkably short space of time it vanished altogether, leaving a final flourish in the western sky which also began to fade quickly away. Not a word passed between the two officers. They glued their eyes to the enemy leaguer and waited. Another quarter of an hour passed with no sign of a car. The brief desert twilight began to creep over the leaguer. Ten minutes later the light was fading in dead earnest. The Major shifted in his seat impatiently. It looked as though the affair might be a wash-out after all. And for the best part of the day he had been working up to this final tit-bit. He began to suffer all the pangs of a good frustration.

Suddenly his spirits took an upward bound. In the fading light he saw yet one more staff car quit the concentration and speed down the track leading from the leaguer. The infantry subaltern had seen it, too.

"Start-up . . ." they yelled as one man to their drivers.

"Quick . . . Get in touch with the O.P.'s and send this message," the Major called over his shoulder to the signaller. "Closing down now . . . We are going to try to winkle a Jerry car before we go home."

"Message received, sir," the signaller announced in a few moments.

"Right . . . Switch off the power . . . Let's go . . ." shouted the Major.

The engines roared, the two carriers burst from their hiding-place still covered with their camouflage of scrub, and careered headlong down the side of the ridge towards the track at the bottom.

"Yoicks! . . . Tally-ho! . . ." yelled the Major, in his excitement.

Half-way down the slope it was evident that they had been seen by their quarry. The staff car accelerated.

"We shall be too late to cut him off," cried the Major. "We'll have to chase him."

They reached the track below the ridge and pelted along on the hard ground beside it, only a few yards behind the German car. In the rear of the carrier the signaller loaded the Bren-gun and trained it on the fugitive.

"Shall I fire, sir?" he asked.

"No . . . Not unless we look like losing him altogether," shouted the Major.

The chase continued in the semi-darkness. It looked as though the carrier might yet overtake the car. In the rush and excitement no one in the carrier paid any attention to the fact that the German officer in the car was leading them round the elbow-bend of the ridge beyond which the track had always been invisible to them, and where the Major had convinced himself that some German H.Q. was located.

Followed at top speed by the carrier the car swung round the bend, and the instant it had done so swerved unexpectedly off the track almost at right-angles to it. And at the same moment the pursuers discovered that instead of having a mere staff car in front of them they were driving directly at three German tanks, stationary, and pointing straight towards them, only two hundred and fifty yards down the track.

" Three tanks ahead, sir," yelled the signaller.

" Seen," said the Major calmly.

There was no need for orders. The driver swung the carrier round in its own length and the vehicle swayed like a boat hit broadside by a heavy wave. Behind them, the second carrier, having already seen the danger, also turned to go back with the subaltern firing a full belt through the Vickers down the track in the direction of the tanks. In the Major's vehicle the signaller reversed the Bren-gun, fired a few rounds and had a jam. While he was endeavouring to get the gun going again the leading tank opened fire. The flash of its gun was followed by an explosion in the rear of the carrier which set the camouflage net and the scrub on top ablaze. A few seconds later the petrol supply caught light. Neither the Major nor the driver up in front realised they were on fire. The signaller stood up to shout a warning. As he did so a burst of machine-gun fire came from the tank. One bullet wounded the signaller slightly in the head, and another in the chest. He was knocked forward over the front of the carrier and tumbled to the ground. The near-side track nearly ran over him.

Glancing over his shoulder the Major now became aware of what had occurred.

" Stop! . . ." he bellowed.

The carrier pulled up in one huge jerk within ten yards. Out jumped the Major followed by the driver. They raced back to where the half-stunned signaller was trying to raise himself from the ground.

"Hit?" asked the Major, briefly.

"Only a graze, sir," replied the signaller, dizzily.

Between them the Major and the driver carried him back, and the three of them took shelter from the machine-gun bullets in front of the blazing carrier. By this time the subaltern's carrier had swung round and returned to pick them up, the Vickers returning the fire of the tank in burst after burst. The wounded signaller was unceremoniously thrown inside. There was no time for niceties. The Major and his driver followed. In a second or two the carrier with its six occupants was racing back the way it had come.

Once round the bend they were free of the attentions of the tank and considered themselves out of pressing danger. Behind them the firing ceased. It was getting really dark now. They struck off the track and commenced to climb the ridge.

"Neat, the way that fellow led us up the garden," observed the subaltern, as the excitement of their escape began to die down. "We got out of it very cheaply."

"I'd think so, too, if I hadn't thrown away a good O.P. for nothing," replied the Major, glumly.

His chagrin was profound. The subaltern decided that this was a case for silent sympathy. He said no more. They headed across the desert and hit the battery just as it was forming up to move into leaguer for the night.

IX—A Skittle in Bomb Alley

The convoy was two days out of Gib. It had slipped quietly through the Straits, shielded by misty weather from prying periscopes and eagle-eyed recce planes. But now it was on full exhibition. The atmosphere was brilliantly clear, the blue sky cloudless. The August sun beat down on the glassy Mediterranean with an almost tropical ferocity.

In their little cabin amidships, just below deck on the 12,000-ton merchantman, the Bofors Sergeant and his lance-bombardier were finding it far too hot to doze, despite the somnolent effects of the excellent lunch they had just demolished. Theirs was an American-built vessel manned by an American crew. And the British A.A. gun crew on board, revelling in the lavish proportions of their American victualling allowance, were only too eager to admit that when it came to a matter of feeding on war service the Yanks knew how to do themselves proud. At dinner the previous evening the Sergeant had counted six courses. Nothing remotely resembling that had ever happened to him in any sergeants' mess during his entire shore service since the war began.

Sweating underneath his khaki overalls and sleeveless life-jacket, the Sergeant lay on his back in his bunk, eyes closed, enumerating with appreciation all the luxuries (mainly out of cans) that had already regaled their table during the nine days at sea.

"And no tea," grumbled the Lance-Bombardier, interrupting the long list, "Coffee . . . coffee . . . coffee . . . Morning, afternoon and night. And no beer, neither. . . ."

"It's a teetotal ship."

"Don't I know it . . . I thought all that Prohibition bunk was dead long ago. Couldn't I do with a can of bitter now!"

"The steward will bring you a drink if you're thirsty."

"Yes . . . Powdered milk and water. . . ."

The Sergeant laughed at the tone of disgust.

"You ought not to have volunteered for the Maritime Service. You don't appreciate its peculiar benefits," he said, unclosing his eyes.

"Such as?"

"Isn't the Maritime Artillery the only regiment still allowed to have its boots polished?"

"And we have to buy the polish ourselves. That *is* a privilege."

"Aren't you allowed a civvy kit so that you can go ashore in neutral ports?"

"Go on, sarge. Make me laugh a lot."

"And suppose your ship is carrying a cargo of iron ore, as often happens. If it's hit you sink like a stone. No waiting."

"I know . . . And if it's petroleum you go up just about as fast. Another bloody fine privilege . . . We're carrying a lot of aviation spirit ourselves, aren't we, sarge?"

"Ours is such a mixed cargo there's no saying what'll happen to us if we get hit," the Sergeant replied, comfortingly.

"Well, we shan't have to wait long before we know," said the Lance-bombardier, after a pause.

He did no more than echo the thought uppermost in the minds of all on board, since the ship had entered the Straits.

The convoy was the largest that had ever attempted to force a passage through to beleaguered Malta. The needs of the staunch little island-buttress of Empire had grown desperate. Every man on board the 12,000-tonner knew that it was a life or death matter.

The First Mate had rubbed it well home just as they were approaching Gib. He called a meeting on deck of all the ship's A.A. gunners and addressed them emphatically.

"Count the pleasure cruise as over," he said. "From now on we'll have to go through hell. But that's nothing to do with it. One job is to smash through to Malta. We've got to get there. That's all."

And now each knot they steamed shortened the distance between them and Bomb Alley, where the hell so confidently predicted by the mate might be expected to take material shape.

The 12,000-tonner's cargo was, as the Sergeant had described it, a mixed one, eloquent of Malta's pressing needs. Deep down in the hold were stored land mines, sea mines, torpedoes, bombs, shells of all calibres and high-grade aviation spirit in sealed containers. On top of this, as a protection, were stores of flour, corned beef, cigarettes and chocolate for the garrison. Above the sealed hatches, as further protection, tons of coal had been stacked in sacks lashed to the hatches. And finally, on top of the coal, were landing-craft, for conveying the stores ashore in case the vessel was unable to come alongside in harbour.

To safeguard these treasures the ship mounted a couple of Oerlikons and a Bofors, in the way of A.A. artillery, and also a surface weapon. The latter, a 4.7 inch on a raised platform to the extreme aft of the ship, was manned by U.S. gunners. The Oerlikons, on either side, also had American crews.

Right forward in the bows of the vessel was the British-manned Bofors, in an inch-steel gunpit, under the command of the Sergeant. Theoretically the Sergeant took his orders from the captain of the ship. But the actual extent of his powers had been clearly conveyed to him in few words by the third mate: " Use your own discretion. You know more about it than we do."

Apart from the Bofors crew the only other British personnel on board were a detachment of Royal Navy signallers, and a naval officer who spent most of his time on the bridge with the captain.

The seven days run to Gibraltar had been quite uneventful. On the way the convoy picked up its escort in groups—a cruiser and two or three destroyers here ; a battleship and more destroyers there ; an aircraft carrier ; another battleship ; another cruiser ; more destroyers ; two more aircraft carriers. And so on. Before they sighted Gib. they had collected altogether six carriers. En route the A.A. gunners were given plenty of practice in mock air battles with planes from the aircraft carriers. And also a taste of what they might expect. . . .

In the stifling cabin amidships the Bofors Sergeant closed his eyes once more. The excellent lunch was at last doing its job. A sweet drowsiness stole over him and hopes of a brief nap revived, if only the Lance-Bombardier didn't disturb him. His hopes were soon dispelled.

" Hear that, sarge ? " asked his companion suddenly.

The Sergeant had heard. Three indistinct muffled reports. . . .

"They're getting the paravanes out forward, in case of mines ahead," he guessed, dreamily.

Hardly had he spoken when a sailor dashed down the companion-way.

"Grab your life-jackets," he shouted. "U-boats . . . A ship's been torpedoed."

The Sergeant swung himself out of his bunk, and almost out of the cabin, in the same movement. He raced towards his Bofors in the fo'castle head with the Lance-Bombardier at his heels. All over the ship electric alarm-bells were clanging. Sailors and gunners were rushing to their action stations, the U.S. navy gunners in tin-hats and bell-bottoms, and in various stages of undress. Orders were being bellowed through megaphones. In an instant the whole ship seemed to have swarmed like an angry hive.

By the time the Sergeant reached his gun the layers were in their seats, the gun was already loaded, and a bombardier, the feeding-number, had taken up his station on the platform, ready to drop new clips of ammunition into the auto-loader. All around, the grand panorama of the convoy provided the eye with the same impressive picture as when the Sergeant had quitted the deck to go to lunch an hour or so before. In the brilliant sunshine merchantmen and warships were steaming steadily over the blue unruffled surface of the Mediterranean resembling more a fleet in review order than one engaged in a desperate adventure. There was the leading cruiser, the same distance ahead of the 12,000-tonner as when the Sergeant last saw it. There was the battleship to their port, another merchant ship to starboard, and the big tanker astern. They did not appear to have altered their relative positions a yard. And the same could be said of all the other vessels, including the aircraft carriers in among the convoy, and the destroyers that formed the ring outside.

But there was one important difference. Looking a mile astern, on the starboard quarter of the convoy, the Sergeant could see one of the aircraft carriers listing badly. It was the torpedoed ship. She had been hit on the port side, and a tall column of white smoke was rising straight from her interior into the windless air. Planes and men were sliding off the tilted landing-deck into the water. Destroyers hovered round picking up survivors. Four Spitfires that had left the carrier at the moment she was torpedoed continued to circle round her like perturbed birds wheeling over their nest that had been destroyed.

The Sergeant searched the sky attentively through his binoculars.

" Not our turn yet," he summed-up to the expectant gun-crew, lowering the glasses. " No Jerry planes about."

The black flag flying from the mast on the port side of the flag-ship was a further indication to them that the present danger was from U-boats, the signal for air attack being red.

The Bofors gunners would have preferred a visible enemy whom they could have struck back at. As it was they kept their eyes glued on the waters, expecting every second to detect the deadly trail of a torpedo racing towards them. No one knew how many U-boats had penetrated the ring, nor where the next blow might fall. The moments were tense with possibilities. Suddenly there sounded a terrific explosion followed by another, and another. Each report seemed to strike the ship's bottom and send a slight shudder through the hull. It was the destroyers on the far side of the convoy already dropping depth-charges. No charges could be dropped in the vicinity of the torpedoed ship. The men in the water would have been killed by the concussion.

On the bridge of the 12,000-tonner, the skipper and the naval commander awaited orders from the flagship.

" Evasive Action. . . ."

The flagship ran up the signal giving the change of course. After a short while down came the signal. A hooter sounded. And immediately all the ships in the convoy turned as one in the direction signalled. Henceforth they progressed in zig-zag fashion, to port and starboard in turn, at the call of the hooter.

Meanwhile, the 12,000-tonner had put out its steel paravanes against mines. Under the direction of the first mate they were lowered over the side by means of a derrick. They floated out just below water-line, about twenty feet each side of the hull, looking for all the world like grey torpedoes trying to race the ship. The Bofors gun-crew had to attune their ears to a new music—the incessant vibrating hum from the steel wires suspending the paravanes from the bows of the ship.

By now the torpedoed aircraft-carrier was merely a swirl of foamy water, well astern, on the otherwise glassy surface of the sea. In half an hour she was no more than a blur of white smoke hanging over the western horizon. Throughout the day the convoy continued its zig-zag course ringed round by the reverberating explosions of the depth charges dropped by the destroyers in case more U-boats were about. But nothing further happened. Night fell. Moonless, and very dark. In the Bofors gun-pit of the 12,000-tonner the gunners took it in turn to stand down and snatch an hour's sleep on the deck.

Next day brought the convoy within the same latitude as the Italian naval bases, which was a matter of some concern to it, because of the possibility of the Italian fleet making an attempt to draw-off the escort. Once more the atmosphere was crystal-clear, with a blue, burning sky confronting a smooth, polished blue sea. Sky and sea met on a far distant horizon which was as sharp and distinct as a line ruled in a copy-book. Morning passed quietly but at mid-day the guns of the escort put up a heavy barrage against a lone plane, flying very high.

"Back she goes, with the names of every one of us," observed the Bofors Sergeant cheerfully, watching through his binoculars the Messerschmitt departing untouched.

The significant change brought about in the situation by the appearance of the reconnaissance plane was quickly reflected by the new dispositions of the escort. Previously it had steamed in a formation suited to counter U-boat attacks. Now it re-arranged itself to meet the expected onslaught from the air. The battleships dropped to the rear of the convoy, the cruisers went to the front, and the aircraft carriers distributed themselves along each side. In this order they progressed steadily for some hours, the distroyers on the outer ring still now and again shattering the blue calm of the afternoon with their depth charges.

Suddenly the look-out man in the Bofors gun-pit shouted:

"Red Flag. . . ."

"Take post . . ." roared the Sergeant, glancing out of the pit towards the flagship which, warned by its R.D.F., had run up its port mast the signal for hostile aircraft.

The gun layers jumped into their seats, and the Bombardier mounted the loading platform, with a couple of gunners crouched at his feet ready to hand up fresh clips of ammunition. The Sergeant raked the clear sky avidly with his binoculars, but it remained empty except for the Spitfires that had ascended in readiness from the aircraft carriers.

Not till just before sunset did the attack develop. Flying very high, from almost due east, twenty-five dive-bombers swooped down on the convoy. They were greeted with an ear-splitting barrage from the heavy A.A. guns of the escort. At the same time the Spitfires went to work to break up the formations. A terrific thunderstorm seemed to develop suddenly in a clear cloudless sky, and the deep boom of artillery and exploding bombs rolled in strange contrast over the placid waters.

"Here's ours . . ." yelled the Sergeant, after the attack had been in progress a few minutes.

A Stuka that had broken formation was diving sheer on them at an angle of eighty-five degrees. The harrowing scream of her fall could be heard even amid the surrounding din.

The Bofors muzzle pointed steeply at the sky above them.

"On . . . On . . ." shouted the layers almost in unison.

"Fire . . ." roared the Sergeant.

The Number Four pressed his foot on the firing-pedal and a stream of shells sped up to meet the descending plane. None of them hit her. And at the same time she dropped her bomb. It fell astern the 12,000-tonner, between them and the big tanker behind, sending up a great fountain of water which drenched them with its spray.

Other guns were now firing at the Stuka. But she had had enough. Dropping to a thousand feet she suddenly flattened out for a moment and then began to climb almost as steeply as she had descended. Hers was almost the last bomb dropped. When the Bofors gunners had time to give attention to the rest of the battle they saw the bombers departing, still pursued by the shells of the big guns. The blue sky was dotted with hundreds of little tufts of white smoke, which hung in the calm air, almost as complete in shape as when first formed by the exploding shells. Between these, several parachutes were gracefully dropping into the sea with pilots who had baled out from hit planes. Astern, and to starboard of the 12,000-tonner, a large merchantman had been hit, but did not appear to be sinking. Its deck was piled with debris and one of the lifeboats dangled over the water from a single pulley. The bomb had fallen amidships and wrecked the bridge. All the controls were gone. The ship lay helpless and motionless on the smooth waters. A couple of destroyers raced in to give assistance. The rest of the convoy steamed away on its course, and soon the falling darkness hid her, and her subsequent fate, from her former companions.

" More blasted coffee ! " suddenly groaned the Lance-bombardier in the Bofors gun-pit.

A couple of stewards laden with trays of sandwiches and coffee pots were bringing up the gunners' evening meal. Gone was the era of six-course dinners. Ever since the sinking of the aircraft carrier the men had been pinned to the gun. And pinned to coffee and sandwiches also !

" What's this ? Breakfast, lunch, tea or dinner ? " the Lance-bombardier enquired of the stewards with gloomy sarcasm. " Dive-bombers or no dive-bombers, I'm bloody well going right through to Malta if only to get a cup of tea."

The night passed quietly. At dawn every gun was fully manned in expectation of an attack. But it wasn't till later in the morning that the red flag again fluttered from the flagship's port mast. Shortly afterwards swarms of Ju. 88's and Ju. 87's came over in waves of fifty, and were met with a storm of shells from the escort's heavy guns. Once more the cannonade rolled over the peaceful sunlit sea like a thunderstorm that had lost its bearings. Spitfires from the carriers hurled themselves headlong against the formations, splitting them into pieces before they could reach the convoy. Nevertheless many solitary planes penetrated the cordon and began their screaming dives upon the merchant ships. To the deep growl of the outer defences was added the bark and snap of the Bofors and Oerlikons.

In the gun-pit on the 12,000-tonner the sweating gunners took on everything that came within range.

"Pom . . . pom . . . pom . . . pom. . . ."

"Pom . . . pom . . . pom . . . pom. . . ."

The characteristic four-time rhythm of the Bofors never ceased. On the loading-platform the bombardier was dropping the clipped shells into the auto-loader as fast as they were handed up to him. The floor of the gun-pit became littered with empty shells cases.

Hundreds of rounds had been fired without a pause when the Sergeant turned and spat heartily on the barrel of the gun. The spittle disappeared instantly in a little wisp of steam.

"Bloody thing's red-hot," he shouted to the bombardier. "Soon as we get a chance we'll change."

The much-needed respite came shortly afterwards. The Junkers, minus fourteen of their number, flew away without having hit a single ship.

"Change barrel . . . Make safe . . ." shouted the Sergeant.

Four of the crew started to remove the worn-out barrel from the gun and lower it by means of a derrick on the deck. Those men not employed on this task were posted in the gun-pit to keep a look-out with binoculars, or detailed to replenish ammunition supplies from the magazine below.

'Changing barrel' in action is always a ticklish business. You can never be sure how much time you will be allowed. The Sergeant grew impatient. He did not want to be caught on the wrong foot. After five minutes he began to cast anxious glances at the horizon. There was no sign yet of another attack. But the red flag still flew from the flagship.

" Hurry yourselves up . . ." he shouted to the men round the derrick. " Are you going to take all day? . . . We're not a shore battery now. If he comes it'll be us he's after."

Three new barrels lay in readiness on deck under the gun-pit. The derrick hoisted one of these into position. A minute or two later the cover-plate closed firmly over the breech ring and the Bofors was ready for the next dive-bomber.

"Ten minutes," announced the Sergeant with satisfaction, glancing at his wrist-watch. " Not so bad. . . ."

Actually they were just in time, for the gun had scarcely been reloaded when the escort's A.A. defences began to pounder again at something on the horizon.

This time the dive-bombers did not arrive alone. They were accompanied by aerial torpedo bombers. While clouds of the former attacked the convoy from overhead, the latter sought to get at it from the sides. These twin-engine bombers, flying quite low, began by trying to penetrate on the port side. Then they swept right round to starboard. Then back to port again, vainly endeavouring to break through the lane of the convoy. The escort's guns on the outer ring kept them out. And finally, giving up the attempt they started to torpedo the Navy ships. Thus two concentric air battles were being waged at the same time. The one round the outer ring, against the torpedo-bombers, and the other inside, where the merchant vessels were vigorously defending themselves against the dive-bombers swooping down from overhead.

It was hotter work than ever. Empty, smoking shell cases again covered the bottom of the Bofors gun-pit on the 12,000-tonner, ankle deep. The atmosphere reeked with the fumes of cordite. The new barrel warmed up till its temperature began to approach that of the one it had displaced. But the Sergeant didn't bother to waste his spittle on it. There could be no question of a change now. A pandemonium filled the air—guns roaring, shells bursting above, bombs and torpedoes bursting below. Amid all this din there was never absent the long drawn out shriek of some plane or other making its dive. Tall, foaming fountains, flung up by bombs exploding in the sea, played in among the convoy, sometimes as many as half a dozen at the same time.

"Take that one . . ." yelled the Sergeant, pointing.

Coming unexpectedly out of the sun a dive-bomber was swooping to bomb the cruiser just in front of them.

The Bofors traversed to meet it.

"On . . . On . . ." shouted the layers.

"Fire . . ." bellowed the Sergeant.

He watched the yellowish-white tracer shells speed upwards. A single puff of grey smoke emerged from the plane. Then it streamed black smoke. The plane crashed into the sea just ahead of them without falling out of its dive.

"Bloody smart work, boys," cried the Sergeant gleefully, patting the layers on the back. "Got him full-on . . . There's another present for you."

The newcomer was travelling directly ahead. He passed them on the port side and as he was getting abeam of the ship the Bofors hit him in the tail. He flattened out, tried to rise but couldn't, and eventually plunged into the sea, astern the convoy.

Elated by this second success the Sergeant raked the sky with his binoculars for a new victim. But nothing more presented itself. Away to starboard fourteen bombers were diving over a carrier. But they were out of range of his gun. He watched the carrier's A.A. guns blow half the dive-bombers to pieces. One of the remainder scored a direct hit. Two great plumes of smoke ascended from the carrier, one amidships, the other astern. She dropped back astern of the convoy with an escort of destroyers. Shortly afterwards the smoke died away as the damage was brought under control.

With this belated success the raiders had to be content. They departed, leaving in the air behind them four parachutes still drifting slowly down to the surface of the sea. The coffee-pots and trays of sandwiches once more made their appearance in the Bofors gun-pit, with the addition of water and powdered milk. This time even the Lance-bombardier had no criticism to offer. Like the rest of the gun crew, his throat was so sore and parched from the cordite fumes he had swallowed during the engagement that he was quite indifferent as to what he poured down it, so long as it was something wet. All of them were, by now, feeling the effects of their recent exertions. Seventy-two hours had passed since the torpedoing of the aircraft carrier. During that time there had been practically no sleep for any of them. They had manned the gun getting on for sixty hours without a break. And the worst of Bomb Alley still lay ahead. . . .

The convoy was now entering the Narrows, between Sicily, Pantellaria and Cape Bon. At this juncture the escort split up. The big ships—battleships and most of the cruisers—said farewell and turned back for Gibraltar. They had done their job, which was to escort the convoy past the danger zone of the enemy naval bases. Henceforth it was the aircraft carriers' pigeon.

"Now the party is really going to begin," commented the Bofors Sergeant as he stood in the gun-pit on the 12,000-tonner watching the gap between the convoy and the big ships widening. And the tired gunners, upon whom not an atom of the significance of the big ships' departure was lost, spurred themselves to a new pitch of alertness.

The afternoon wore on. The lull before the storm lasted till after five o'clock. Then it broke with a fury transcending all previous efforts. Wave upon wave of dive-bombers swooped down on the convoy. Scores of aerial torpedo bombers attacked it along each side.

This time they managed to break through the outer cordon, and flew down the lane of the convoy, just above the surface of the water, launching their torpedoes. The calm sea was hurled high in great waterspouts as they exploded. In very little time a couple of ships had been hit and were listing badly.

Being the leading merchant vessel in the convoy, the 12,000-tonner seemed to be first pick for dive-bombers and torpedoes alike. In the Bofors gun-pit the layers never ceased traversing and elevating in all directions. One moment the gun was pointing upwards at an angle of seventy-five degrees, sending a stream of shells towards a plane screaming down upon them from a tremendous altitude. A second or two later it flattened almost horizontal in order to take-on a torpedo-bomber flying at them mast-high.

The look-out man posted in the rear of the gun-pit kept them informed of urgent cases.

" Torpedo-plane to port . . ." he yelled.

The Bofors gave a tail-less dive-bomber a parting burst and swung round to meet the new peril. But before the layers could get the torpedo-bomber in their sights the Sergeant shouted :

" There goes his fish. . . ."

The torpedo glided into the water. Glancing over the side of the gun-pit, the gunners saw the deadly white streak on the surface coming straight for them. Before they had time to give themselves up for lost the ship lurched violently to port. On the bridge the skipper had also seen the danger, and just managed to avoid it. The torpedo sped past them. A few seconds later there was a terrific explosion. A merchant ship astern had been hit by their torpedo. Her bows were smashed and she began to sink rapidly.

What with torpedo-bombers roaring up and down the lane of the convoy, and dive-bombers never ceasing their attacks from aloft, it became a matter of every ship for itself. Merely on the score of self-protection the Bofors Sergeant found it necessary to make discriminations. They could do no more than fire at the planes which spelt imminent danger to themselves personally. The Sergeant stood by the gun judiciously selecting his targets :

" Let that one go. He's finished with us. . . ."

" Get that one before he gets us. . . ."

Wherever he pointed the muzzle of the gun immediately followed.

There came a yell from the look-out man.

" Plane from astern, sarge. . . ."

The Sergeant grabbed the big traversing handle at the rear of the gun and spun it round a complete arc of one hundred and eighty degrees.

" On. . . . On . . ." shouted the layers.

" Fire. . . ."

They missed. But the plane swerved away from the ship and cut across the convoy.

Back spun the gun to meet a torpedo-bomber coming down the lane of the convoy, almost skimming the water. Their first burst sent it under the surface.

"Plane two-points to starboard. . . ."

Again the gun swung round.

This one, travelling at a tremendous speed, they missed. But the ship behind them got it. The plane crashed, skidded for a long way on the top of the water under the impetus of its speed, and then dived out of sight.

So the battle continued without a break. Dusk fell and the Bofor's tracers now went up like purple balls of fire. Within the area of the convoy the surface of the water was whipped up by the shrapnel of the A.A. shells as if by a torrential rain. The sky was rarely vacant of falling planes and parachutes. Half-a-dozen or more merchant ships in various stages of dissolution had dropped astern the convoy. The escort, too, had had its losses.

Immediately astern the 12,000-tonner the sea itself seemed to be on fire. The big tanker that had been their immediate companion since the voyage began had been hit by a torpedo. She was a mass of towering flame from stem to stern. Not a glimpse of the ship itself could be seen. Just one great angry blaze. The Bofors gunners on the 12,000-tonner could feel the heat of her on their faces.

But she persisted in keeping afloat, lighting up the darkness like a huge torch and giving the bombers a grand last chance against the silhouetted ships. Aware of this danger the convoy speeded-up to relieve themselves of her undesirable proximity.

And with darkness enveloping them, the long attack at last ended.

Coffee and sandwiches. . . .

The Bofors crew fell-to with all the light-hearted zest of victorious warriors whose battles were o'er. They felt confident that having survived the grand assault they had nothing more to fear.

"I'll have the biggest pot of tea in Malta, to-morrow. All to myself," observed the Lance-bombardier, sternly addressing his second mug of coffee as if it were an old offender.

The ensuing stretch of two hours peace and quiet flattered their feelings of security. These were further strengthened a little later when a light beaconed them from the African coast. It was Cape Bon lighthouse, a welcome landmark in their travail. Now they entered on the last lap. The convoy altered course. Henceforth they sailed on a straight line to Malta. Under cover of the friendly darkness the Sergeant considered himself justified in allowing his weary men the chance of a sleep. Three gunners remained in the gun-pit, keeping watch. The rest stretched themselves out on the deck below.

The cruiser ahead of them dispelled their dreams. Suddenly it began to sweep the dark sea with its searchlights.

Then, without warning, the guns of the escort opened fire at something on the water.

" Take Post . . ." roared the Sergeant.

"What is it now, sarge ?" inquired the Lance-bombardier, tumbling into the gun-pit.

" E-boats. . . ."

In the white glare of the searchlights the Sergeant had caught a glimpse of two of them, like miniature destroyers, whipping along at great speed inside the convoy, and trying to get the ships silhouetted against the Cape Bon light. All the vessels of the escort were now using their searchlights, firing at every E-boat they spotted.

The attack had not been in progress long before the ears of the Bofors crew were deafened by a shattering explosion. The cruiser ahead had been hit by a torpedo amidships. Its searchlights were extinguished as if suddenly snuffed out. In the immediate darkness the 12,000-tonner managed to steer round her and continued on its course behind a couple of destroyers that were mine-sweeping in front.

They had left the cruiser about a mile astern when a gunner shouted excitedly :

" Look out . . . There's a torpedo. . . ."

Staring over the side of the gun-pit they could see the thin streak of foam that was racing towards them. It was only twenty yards away, coming straight for the bows. On the bridge the skipper had also seen it, and tried to swerve from its path. He just failed to clear. The torpedo hit the ship right beneath the gun-pit.

Instinctively, every man within ducked. First they heard the thud against the hull. There followed a pause that seemed eternal to their straining ears, but which was merely a matter of a second or two. Then came the roar of the explosion as the magazine blew up.

The gunners were hurled across the gun-pit in all directions. When they had recovered from the shock, and picked themselves up out of the heap of empty shell cases, they found themselves surrounded by a fog of fumes and half-choked by the acrid reek of cordite. The ship had listed heavily to starboard, and they staggered about to find their balance. An extraordinary death-like quiet seemed to have descended upon the ship. They could not hear a sound.

As their deafened ears recovered, the ship's life stole on their consciousness again. But an unusual confused life.

Now they could hear hoarse shouts in the darkness, sounds of feet running along the decks from all directions, and occasionally men cursing. Then orders being bellowed through megaphones for all on board to proceed to their lifeboat stations.

"Come on, boys . . . That means us, too," shouted the Sergeant to his half-stunned crew.

They clambered out of the gun-pit and picked their way with difficulty among the disordered cargo on deck towards their lifeboat amidships.

Stewards were bawling out in the darkness.

"Canteen's wide open. Take what you want . . . Canteen's wide open. Help yourself. . . ."

The Sergeant hesitated. He felt very hungry. One of his reactions after intense excitement was always intense appetite. He thought of the long hours they might have to spend in the lifeboat. . . .

On the other hand the ship was listing badly. True, she was settled on an even keel. But she was going down all right. There would be a risk. . . .

"Life's sweeter than chocolate," he decided. And he doubled-up after the others to the lifeboat.

* * *

The lifeboat, laden with the Bofors gun crew and the detachment of Royal Navy signallers, pulled away from the torpedoed ship at half-past two in the morning. At nine-thirty a.m., the Lance-bombardier, huddled in the centre of the boat with the Sergeant, heard a straggling cheer forward.

"Who scored?" he inquired, wearily.

"Couple of our destroyers coming up," replied the Sergeant.

"Thank God for that," said the Lance-bombardier fervently. "I'm dying for a cup of tea. . . ."

X—Malayan Gun-site

Inside the attap-roofed hut which did double duty as Officers' Mess and Command Post of the section of 3-inch static guns engaged in defending the airfield a few miles south of the Thailand border, the broad-shouldered, heavy-browed Lieutenant suddenly stopped eating his bully-beef and tinned peas and began scratching his back ferociously. His companion, the Captain in command of the section, helped himself liberally to tinned pineapple.

"If you scratch much more, old chap, I shall fancy I've got a dose myself and start scratching, too," he protested.

The Lieutenant's naked back and stomach were decorated with a mass of tiny, fiery-looking pustules which itched maddeningly. He had arrived on the gun-site from Singapore only two days before, when it was clear that the Japanese were commencing hostilities against the Malayan Peninsula by a landing in the northern province of Kelantan. And he had at once fallen a victim to a bad attack of prickly heat. For the last thirty-six hours his existence had been pretty equally divided between the tortures of his pimples and the discomforts of Japanese dive-bombing attacks. And he knew which he preferred. He was a powerfully-built, burly fellow who had been commissioned at Singapore from the ranks two years before war broke out in the East. His characteristics were a large hooked nose and a passion for Mah Jong. He had brought his cherished tiles with him to the airfield hoping for the best. But the box remained in his kit unopened, under the combined influence of prickly heat and air raids. Which also added to his irritation.

He received the Captain's mild protest with a scowl.

" I'm not scratching myself for fun," he said. " Perhaps you'll be good enough to suggest what I ought to do."

" They say rain-water is a fine thing to take the sting out of it."

" Have you any rain about you ? " replied the Lieutenant with heavy sarcasm.

The tall, slim Captain laughed.

" Try some of this pine-apple," he said. " You'll find it not unrefreshing."

The temperature was ninety-five degrees in the shade, and to wear a tin-hat was not unlike carrying about a small furnace on top of one's head. A sticky, humid heat with a fierce sun beating down from a brilliant blue sky unspecked by the faintest wisp of cloud. A mile or so distant from the airfield, and separated from it by a strip of jungle and a stretch of sandy dunes, was the smooth oily sea, blue as the sky above and, from the point of view of refreshing breezes, about as unsympathetic.

The section formed part of an Indian H.A.A. regiment. Its four guns were mounted forty yards from each other at the extreme south-east corner of the airfield, their pedestals bolted to concrete platforms. Not far behind stood a couple of attap huts, a large one where the Punjabi gun detachments lived, and a smaller one which was now occupied by the two officers, the only white men on the site. There was a third hut some distance to the rear of the others. This was set apart as a kind of mosque for the Indian gunners and N.C.O.'s. Here were kept the prayer mats on which they knelt and turned their faces towards Mecca at sunrise and sunset when the havildar (sergeant) who undertook the function of muezzin wailed out his call to prayer.

The airfield itself had only been in existence a few months and was still far from finished. It had been constructed as one of the most northerly in Malaya from which to bomb enemy bases in Thailand and Indo-China in the event of war with Japan. Roughly, it took the shape of a rectangle, a mile long and three-quarters of a mile broad. On the northern verge, in the direction from which the Japanese infantry were now advancing, stood the administrative buildings, chiefly attap huts and very inflammable. A dozen smallish hangars, eight of which were merely temporary affairs—canvas stretched over wooden frames, and camouflaged in black, green and khaki—dotted the western end of the field, with the bomb magazine in the south-west corner. The petrol storage-tanks were on the opposite side of the field, about a hundred yards from the gun positions. The runway, a strip of tarmac thirty yards wide, cut north and south down the centre of the rough, sandy surface of the field for half-a-mile.

Virgin jungle had been cleared to make room for the airfield, and virgin jungle still enclosed it on all sides except to the north. Here the ground was covered with a thick scrub, not much more penetrable than the jungle itself.

Jungle to the depth of two miles separated the airfield on its western side from a road running south from the northern tip of the province.

The battle for the possession of this northern gateway leading into the Peninsula was now in its final stages. After an initial repulse the Japanese had succeeded in landing strong forces on the Kelantan coast and were now hurling them, regardless of cost, against the troops of the 9th Indian Division who endeavoured to bar their progress south. Away to the north of the airfield, where the fighting was fiercest, the boom of artillery and the sharp rattle of machine-gun and rifle fire never ceased.

Smoke from burning villages and towns began to spread a haze over the sunlit sky.

At the present moment, the airfield itself displayed marked signs of the attention it had received from the Japanese bombers since the commencement of the battle. All the previous day, and throughout this particular morning, it had been attacked remorselessly by formation after formation of Mitsubishi 97's from their newly-acquired bases just over the Thailand frontier. Here and there on the airfield the skeleton of a Brewster-Buffalo fighter, or a Wirraway biplane, hit while grounded, still smouldered. Several of the hangars had been destroyed, and the attap huts burned out. The whole field was eloquently pock-marked with bomb craters, many of them on the tarmac runway itself. Some of the worst of these had been hastily filled in. But as fast as repairs were done new craters were made. It was quite impossible to keep pace with the damage. Moreover, besides the planes destroyed on the ground, operational losses since the battle began had sadly depleted the mixed assortment of two-score or so of Blenheim bombers, Brewster-Buffalo fighters, and Wirraway reconnaissance planes which comprised the total strength of the airfield when war broke out. The two Gunner officers had not failed to notice that there had been a considerable drop in the number of planes that had set off during that morning to bomb the Japanese transports which were still pouring troops on to the coast. And some of these planes had not returned.

The gun-site itself had not come through the ordeal of the past thirty-six hours unscathed. Craters pitted the ground around the position. Three newly-heaped mounds in the jungle-clearing not far from the attap huts betokened the graves of Punjabi gunners who had been killed by anti-personnel bombs during a raid that very morning. Four other men, badly wounded, had been despatched by lorry to the nearest dressing station eight miles away.

It was now nearly three o'clock in the afternoon, the first opportunity the gun crews had had since dawn to get a decent meal. In front of the big attap hut the Indian cook presided over a large highly-burnished copper cauldron, suspended over a wood fire, from which he ladled out into the gunners' old-fashioned, round mess tins a thick soup made of a mixture of vegetables, and having the density and hue of cream spinach. The Punjabis squatted around in their khaki-drill and bush hats consuming the contents of the cauldron in conjunction with the inevitable flat, round, unsweetened chupattis, to which they helped themselves liberally from freshly-cooked piles stacked near the cauldron.

In the smaller hut the two white officers of the section, waited on by a Chinese boy, were also taking advantage of the lull to snatch a meal. They were in touch by telephone with the local Observer Corps and also with the R.A.F. Headquarters on the airfield. Apart from this they had no communication with the outside world at all. The nearest other H.A.A. section to theirs was the mobile 3.7 inch one in action at Kuala Tregannu, and that was seventy miles or more to the south. Except for scraps of information they picked up by telephoning the Station Adjutant at the R.A.F. Headquarters on the far side of the field they were completely in the dark as to how the battle was going. They certainly were not receiving any encouragement to regard the prospects as very rosy. The last time the Command Post had rung up the R.A.F. Adjutant the reply had been :

" Reconnaissance has just reported the Japs appear to be putting masses of stuff ashore. Things don't look too healthy."

Besides which they had the evidence of their own eyes and ears. Every hour the Gunners could hear the noise of the battle moving steadily nearer and nearer towards them from the north. The cloud of smoke that hung over the battle area increased in density as its distance diminished.

From the way things were going it seemed only a question of a few hours before the airfield, and they themselves, would be overrun.

Some such disturbing thoughts were uppermost in the Captain's mind as he finished his tinned pine-apple. The Lieutenant was far too absorbed by his pestilential pustules to have thoughts for anything else at the moment.

Suddenly the Punjabi telephonist in the Command Post shouted:

"Wanted on the phone, sahib."

"Who is it?" inquired the Captain.

"Station Adjutant, sahib."

The Captain rose and went over to the telephone. When he returned he had gloomy tidings written all over him.

"What's new?" inquired the Lieutenant, ceasing to scratch.

"The R.A.F. are going," the Captain replied briefly.

"Going? Going for good? . . ."

"Yes."

"When?"

"Now."

"Hell . . . That doesn't sound too healthy."

"They've decided the field is untenable and that they can't do any more good by staying here," continued the Captain.

"I'm not surprised. They've had a hell of a pasting. It would have been different if only we'd had a few Spitfires . . . But what about us? Are we going, too? I hope so."

"We stay. For the time being."

"Damn it. . . . Why?"

"To cover the ground staff while they pack up all the equipment they can shift, and destroy the rest."

"I hope they won't take long over it," said the Lieutenant with fervour. "I do wish we knew a bit more about what is going on in front."

"Probably wouldn't ease our minds much."

There sounded the sudden roar of engines outside. The two officers walked to the doorway of the hut and gazed across the airfield. The few planes remaining were already taking-off. One after another they rose into the air, circled the field for the last time, and flew off to their new bases southwards. The Captain and the Lieutenant stood watching them in silence.

The last plane faded from sight over the top of the distant jungle.

"I'd hoped to have some Mah Jong with those fellows,"

said the Lieutenant mournfully. " Makes me feel quite lonely now they've gone."

" Yes. We've got it all to ourselves now. Or soon shall have," replied the Captain, thoughtfully.

Away on the far side of the airfield the R.A.F. lorries were being hastily loaded-up. Fires began to blaze where the stuff that could not be shifted was being destroyed to prevent it falling into the hands of the enemy.

" Hear that burst of machine-gun fire ? " exclaimed the Lieutenant.

The Captain nodded. There was no doubt about the swiftness with which the battle was moving their way. It helped him to come to a decision.

" I think I'll evacuate our spares," he said. " No use all of us hanging round here. They can get a lift in the R.A.F. lorries as far as our wagon-lines and wait there for the rest of us."

He ordered the havildars to detail four complete crews to remain behind to man the guns, and to send the remainder of the section, including the cooks and the Chinese boys, across to the departing lorries. Before quitting the gun-site the Punjabis collected their prayer-mats from the ' mosque.' Laden with these, and led by a stalwart naik (bombardier) they made their way, in a heat that had become more oppressive than ever, across the airfield to the R.A.F. lorries.

Suddenly the Lieutenant grabbed the Captain by the arm.

" Look . . . Over there . . ." he exclaimed in excitement, pointing to the south-west corner of the sky. A few scattered white clouds were just appearing over the top of the jungle in the distance.

" I don't know what that is a sign of up here in Kelantan," he continued, " but down in Singapore you could bet your last dollar you were in for a *Sumatra*."

" I hope we aren't," said the Captain. " As if we haven't got enough trouble on our hands already . . . We'll have the gun-site flooded. And the airfield, too."

" Oh, damn all that. What does it matter ? Aren't we leaving, anyhow ? Let the rain come. Buckets of it. Didn't you tell me just now that rain was the thing to cure my blasted itch. I hope there's no mistake about those clouds."

There was no mistake. The white clouds were the forerunners of a sudden storm which answered to all the Lieutenant's requirements. Soon they were succeeded by heavier clouds, no longer white but grey, which rapidly spread over the sky. The blue heavens turned black, the sun was blotted out, and the earth became wrapped in a sort of livid twilight. Suddenly a vivid flash of lightning leaped from the darkened sky, accompanied by a terrific crack of thunder. As though upon this given signal the heavens opened and poured forth a flood of such dimensions as would have made old Noah glad of his ark. The rain fell in sheets. It was more than mere rain. It came down like a cataract. The dry ground hissed and resounded under the impact. And all the time the lightning continued to flash and the voluminous thunder roared.

At the first indications of the approaching storm the Indian gunners fastened covers over the muzzles and breeches of the guns and retreated to their attap hut where they beguiled the time in singing native songs in a high-pitched nasal tone, songs that seemed to have endless verses and to be inspired by a melancholy that was not particularly cheerful hearing as a counterpoint to the wild beat of the rain. So thought the Captain sheltering in the Command Post, while the victim of prickly-heat, stripped naked, kept on darting from the hut, out of sight of the Indian gunners so as not to lose 'prestige,' to let the deluge beat upon his tormented flesh. In a second or two he would scurry inside again, half-drowned, and spluttering like a man up from a deep dive. Respectable pools of water formed on the earth floor of the hut where the rain drained off him. Then, having regained his breath, he would dart out again for another dose of the cure.

The storm took nearly an hour to exhaust itself. It ended as suddenly as it began. Without any diminution in their violence the thunder and lightning ceased. The waterfall was switched off. The clouds vanished as if by magic. The sun resumed its dominion in a brilliant blue sky. The airfield, water-logged to a depth of several inches, steamed like a vast geyser.

As soon as the skies cleared the gun crews emerged from their hut and splashed back over the flooded ground to clear up the mess the storm had made of the gun positions. The Lieutenant, who was Gun Position Officer, put on his clothes and followed them. His pustules certainly seemed much less irritating. He bore a kindly feeling for the storm which even the unpleasant sight of the water-logged gun-pits did not dissipate.

The gunners had just removed the covers from the breeches of the guns when the telephone in the Command Post buzzed.

"Raid Alarm . . ." shouted the Punjabi operator.

The Captain, megaphone in hand, ran to the doorway of the hut.

"Take Post . . ." he roared to the section.

Over the phone, from the Observer Corps, was coming further details of the impending raid.

"Hostile . . . Nine plus . . . Bearing, Three-One-O . . ." shouted the Command Post Officer to the guns, giving them some idea of the number of raiders they would have to cope with and the rough direction from which they were approaching.

At the same time the section spotters, from their station alongside the predictor and Goetz height-finder, thirty yards behind the guns, were busy scouring the sky with binoculars and T.I. (telescope identification) for a first glimpse of the raiders.

There they came . . . Flying from the north-west. Nine Mitsubishi Army 97's. As they drew nearer the naik at the T.I. could distinguish the solid red circle painted on their wings.

"Nine Ninety-sevens, sahib," he shouted to the Gun Position Officer.

The height-finder and the predictor picked them up at once, and as the No. 1 on the former called out the varying height of the planes so it was put on to the predictor.

In each of the four gun-pits, sitting on either side of the gun, the two Punjabi layers, dark-faced and impassive, meticulously turned the handles of their elevating and traversing dials to synchronise with the movements of the predictor and so keep the guns all the time on the target.

" Fifteen-thousand . . ." shouted the lance-naik at the height-finder.

" Fifteen-thousand set . . ." came the reply almost immediately from the predictor. It was followed shortly afterwards by a shout from the No. 1.

" On Target. . . ."

The No. 4 on the predictor, peering through a little window at the fuse-drum, commenced to chant in a sing-song, nasal tone the numbers of the fuses as they appeared in view.

" Nineteen . . . Eighteen . . . Seventeen . . . Sixteen. . . ."

Estimating the next to be the correct fuse for opening fire he shouted :

" Fifteen . . . Fire. . . ."

During this time each fuse-setter in the gun-pits, nursing a 3-inch shell in the crook of his arms, had been turning its fuse ring to coincide with each of the numbers called out. Directly he heard the word " Fire . . ." he tightened the fuse-ring at the number fifteen, and passed the shell into the leather-gloved hands of the loader who slipped it into the breech.

The four breeches closed behind the shells. The four guns were ready for their initial welcome to the raiders.

" Fire . . ." shouted the four havildars, almost in unison.

The guns roared their salvo. The four shells screamed up into the clear, blue sky. Four tiny white puffs appeared in the path of the raiders.

As was the way with the Japanese pilots in the early raids of the war they displayed complete indifference to the gun-fire. They kept steadily to their course, flying in triangular formation, without weaving or taking any evasive action whatsoever. The lance-naik at the height-finder continued to shout new figures as the height changed.

" Seventeen-thousand . . . Sixteen-thousand . . . Fifteen-thousand . . . Fourteen-thousand-five-hundred. . . ."

At each change a new angle of sight was obtained from the computer on top of the predictor. As the height and angle of sight altered so the No. 4 on the predictor yelled out a new fuse number. It became hot work in the gun-pits. The fuse changed about every four shells. And the guns were firing at the rate of about twenty-four rounds a minute each.

The sky in the quarter of the raiders was now patterned with tiny woolly tufts that, in the windless air, remained almost in the same positions as when the shells first burst. Untouched by the barrage the triangle of Mitsubishis swept on until they were right over the airfield. Watching attentively through his binoculars the Command Post Officer saw a white light suddenly flash from the leading plane. At first he thought it had been hit. Next moment he realised that the light was intended as a signal. The instant it flashed all the planes opened their bomb-doors and out rained the bombs.

The whole airfield trembled under the concussion of the explosions. The bombs fell on the hangars, on the few remaining attap huts on the north side of the field, on some planes already wrecked in the morning's raids, and on the already deeply-cratered runway. Shrapnel sang all round the gun-pits as anti-personnel bombs exploded. Others burst with a white-hot splash. These were phosphorus bombs and they set fire to what was left of the hangars and attap huts.

In the gun-pits the lean, dark-skinned Punjabis toiled away with a steady rhythm like bits of the gun mechanism itself. As fast as the breeches closed the shells screamed upwards with a mounting fury. After releasing their bombs the planes passed over the gun-site, flew some distance over the jungle behind, circled, and then swept back again. Once more the Command Post Officer saw the leader flash his white light. This time, however, the signal had different results. The planes behind him moved into échelon formation.

"They are going to dive," the C.P.O. roared through the megaphone to the guns.

"Independent firing . . ." shouted the Gun Position Officer without an instant's delay.

On each gun the havildar who was the No. 1 took over command. The fuse lengths of the shells were cut down to No. 6. High above them the leading plane peeled off from the formation and commenced its dive. The four guns, loaded and ready to fire, waited for the crucial moment. Down dropped the plane with a piercing scream that grew in intensity as it approached the ground. It looked as though nothing would stop it but the ground itself. Down, down it dropped with no diminution of speed. Suddenly, when not much more than five hundred feet above their heads it released a bomb, gave a sort of convulsive shudder, flattened out for a second or two, and then commenced to climb back steeply into the sky. This was the moment the gunners had been waiting for, when the bomber exposed for a brief while its belly as a target.

"Fire . . ." roared the four havildars, practically at the same instant.

The shells burst close round the ascending plane but without effect. Meanwhile there could be heard the ever-growing shriek of the second plane, half-way down its dive. Then the next . . . And the next. . . .

"They're after the bomb-dump, damn 'em," the Lieutenant muttered to himself, as he stood behind the guns watching the effect of the explosions. "If they hit that we shall hear about it."

However, his dreads were not to be realised. The nine Mitsubishis, having unloaded their bombs, flew off unharmed, leaving the bomb-dump intact but the airfield a burning, smoking, crater-studded desolation. It had all happened in less than two minutes. But it was a two minutes that seemed like an hour.

The guns ceased firing. The Lieutenant walked across to the pits to see how the crews had fared. All things considered, it wasn't too bad. Four gunners and a lance-naik had been wounded, two in the head, two in the shoulder and one, more seriously, in the leg. But there was nothing that a shell-dressing couldn't cope with, for the time being, at any rate.

In the curious atmosphere of quiet that seemed to take possession of the airfield at the end of the two minutes' inferno the Lieutenant, beginning to find his ears working again, became sharply aware again of the noise of the battle to the north. The rifle and machine-gun fire seemed to have approached to within a mile of them. It sounded almost on top of them. Alarmingly close . . . Turning round as he felt something touch him, he found the Command Post Officer at his elbow, looking very worried and serious indeed.

"Our infantry are beginning to come through," said the C.P.O.

He pointed away to the far end of the field in the direction of the battle. In ones and twos and scattered parties, little khaki-clad figures in bush-hats were emerging from the belt of thick scrub and secondary jungle fringing the top of the airfield, and scurrying across it to the thicker cover of the jungle on either side. The Lieutenant recognised them as Dogras from the Indian Division that had been holding the defence line to the north. They looked utterly worn-out and exhausted after their long spell of bitter fighting. As if to add to the gloomy significance of their appearance, stray bullets began to whizz across the airfield and sing round the ears of the gunners in the gun-pits. Smoke was spreading in a flat pall over all the field, partly from the fires caused by the latest bombing and partly from the dumps of material set alight by the R.A.F. ground staff before retiring. It became difficult to see clearly across the field.

All at once, a hundred yards from the gun-pits, the earth itself seemed to burst into flames. One of the last bombs dropped in the attack just over had scored a hit on the petrol tanks. The oil, flowing out on to the field still flooded by the recent storm, had caught light. A wide-spreading lake of fire, with flames a yard high, began slowly to creep towards the gun-pits.

"How much longer are we going to stay here?" demanded the Lieutenant impatiently. "Till we're cooked?"

"We're getting out now," replied the Captain. "The last R.A.F. lorry has just gone. So our job is done. We'll clear out as soon as we have put the guns out of action. We haven't the time to blow them up. But we'll bitch 'em up as much as possible and take away the breech blocks. Smash the predictor dials, and all the instruments. . . . You take the right-hand sub-section. I'll take the left . . . When you have done all the damage make for the edge of the jungle behind the bomb-dump . . . I'll do the same . . . Whoever gets there first will wait for the other . . . Then we'll cut through the jungle until we meet the road running south. There is a narrow track. Come on, now . . . Or the Japs will be all round us. . . ."

There was little need to impress on the Lieutenant the need for speed. The lake of fire had crept to within fifty yards of the gun-site and tongues of petrol-flames were still licking their way forward. The heat grew more intense than ever on their faces. The stray bullets that had begun to whizz about the airfield developed into something resembling sustained rifle fire. Louder and louder sounded the confused shouting, yells, and shots in the belt of scrub on the north side of the field amid which the enemy forward infantry were crushing the final stand of isolated parties of the Indian troops.

The Lieutenant ran to his sub-section.

" Havildar, take the breech-block out . . . Quick! . . ." he shouted to each of the Numbers One.

Losing not a moment the havildars hammered away with mallets to knock out the pins holding the blocks.

The Command Post Officer raced across to the sub-section on the left to superintend the work of destruction there.

It was now sunset, and soon the light would go altogether. Already the airfield was obscured by volumes of smoke from burning hangars and huts through which the flames glared luridly. The petrol lake had spread to the Command Post and the big attap hut used by the Punjabi gunners, and both were blazing furiously.

By now the havildars of the right sub-section had removed the breech-blocks from the two guns and, nursing them in their arms, stood with the gun crews grouped round them awaiting the final order. The predictor dial and all the instruments had been smashed. Taking a last look round to see that all possible damage had been done the Lieutenant shouted:

" Follow me. . . ."

As arranged, he made for the edge of the jungle near the bomb-dump in the south-west corner of the field. The two gun detachments hurried behind him, helping along their wounded companions. On the way they were joined by a detachment from one of the guns of the left sub-section, with the havildar carrying the breech-block. As he stumbled along under the burden he drew out the firing pin and flung it away so as to render the breech-block useless in case he was captured.

They reached the edge of the jungle in safety, and halted a few yards inside to await the arrival of the Captain and the fourth gun detachment. They waited two or three minutes but he did not appear. The Lieutenant began to feel uneasy. The smoke was rolling so thickly over the field that it prevented him from seeing what was happening over at the gun-site. He thought that possibly the Captain had missed the direction in the fog. He went forward some distance and shouted: " Over here . . ." But there was no response. Neither did the Captain show up.

Suddenly the smoke cleared a little over the gun-site. Through the rift the Lieutenant caught a momentary glimpse of the tall figure of the Captain tugging desperately at the breech of a gun assisted by a havildar. Evidently the breech-block had jammed and they were having great difficulty in removing it. The Lieutenant had no time to see anything else before the smoke shut out the view again.

The airfield was now alive with an uproar of sounds—screams, strange yells, cries of exultation, and shots. There was no longer any doubt that it had been overrun. Fearful for the fate of his comrade the Lieutenant strained his eyes to pierce the thick veil that hung between him and the gun-site. But he could see nothing.

More vital seconds passed. And the exultant shouts on the airfield grew in volume as the screams grew fewer. The Punjabis, crouched around the Lieutenant within the edge of the jungle, waited in solemn silence. Half-a-minute went by. Still no sign of the Captain and the fourth detachment.

" For God's sake, old chap, leave the bloody thing and run . . ." the Lieutenant shouted at the top of his voice as the suspense became intolerable.

He was half-a-mile from the gun-site, and amid the din

it was impossible for him to be heard. But he shouted out of sheer desperation.

A few seconds later the smoke again rolled away from the gun-site and the Lieutenant was vouchsafed another glimpse of the Command Post officer. His last. . . .

Silhouetted against the red flames of the burning attap huts the tall, slim figure of the Captain could be seen slowly walking away from the gun that had given him so much trouble. Not walking in the direction of the Lieutenant and his party, but away from them. Nor was he alone. He walked surrounded by half-a-dozen much shorter figures. Japanese. . . .

Then the smoke blotted out the scene once more, leaving the Lieutenant staring stonily in front of him.

"The Captain sahib has been captured. . . ."

The low, sorrowful whisper of the havildar at his side recalled the Lieutenant to the exigencies of the moment. They all stood a good chance of sharing the same fate if they didn't get a move on.

"Yes," he said, bitterly, rising to his feet. "Come along, now . . . Follow me. . . ."

They plunged into the jungle in search of the track leading to the road on which they hoped to find their lorries awaiting them.

XI—Private Amadu Frafra Obeys Orders

It was on a fine sunny morning in the Spring of 1939 that Amadu Frafra booked himself a front seat in the World War. But he did not know it at the time. He had wandered all the way down the Tamale–Kumasi road and, with nothing better to do, was now lounging around the Kumasi barracks square, between the European and Native quarters of the town. In the bright sunshine the drill ground presented an attractive picture with its red laterite surface, like a huge hard tennis-court, its fringe of flame-of-the-forest trees with their green feathery foliage, and the whitewashed barrack buildings on the opposite side. But Amadu Frafra's interest lay not in the picturesque. What he found really worthy of his attention were the squads of native soldiers who, when shouted at by the drill sergeant, all suddenly moved in the same direction at the same time, or came to a halt like one man, or sloped their rifles over their shoulders with a unanimity so unnatural to Amadu that he found it irresistibly comic to watch. Amadu peeled another tooth-stick and settled down to enjoy this excellent show while he leisurely polished his teeth.

He was a well-built coal-black youth of about twenty-three, barefooted and clad in a loincloth. Parts of his skull had been shaven in such a way as to leave his short frizzy hair in the shape of a scorpion. Of this decoration he was inordinately proud. On each of his cheek-bones he bore the broad tribal markings that had been cut in his flesh at birth. He had wandered down to Kumasi from a bush village in the Northern Territories, begging his food day by day at the little native farms where, according to custom, he was always welcome to eat as much as he could, but not allowed to take any away. He was happy because he had nothing to do and nowhere to go.

Two hours passed and Amadu Frafra was more absorbed than ever by the amusing doings on the parade ground. Nothing escaped his big eyes. He had thrown away his tooth-stick, and his magnificent teeth glistened in the sun as he continually spread his mouth in a wide grin. He seemed to be enjoying some huge joke with himself. He also seemed to be on the look-out for something. A little later he saw what he wanted. A white sergeant appeared from one of the barrack buildings and crossed the parade ground. Amadu walked up to him, his grin more expansive than ever.

"He fit to become soldier," he said. By 'he' Amadu meant himself.

The sergeant took him in from head to foot, with one quick skilled glance, and agreed with Amadu's diagnosis. Those were the days when the regiment was free to pick and choose, and the sergeant preferred his raw material to come from the tribes north of the Volta River. He nodded amiably. Amadu's eyes rolled, and his teeth flashed in delight.

They encased Amadu's big feet in a pair of barge-toed boots. They gave him a khaki slouched hat, a pair of khaki-drill long shorts which came below the knee, like Victorian drawers minus the torchon, and a round-necked, collar-less blouse of the same material, which hung like a shirt outside his shorts. Thus equipped he appeared next day in one of the squads on the red barrack square, for instruction in the art of forming threes and sloping arms automatically the instant the native drill sergeant barked, even though his thoughts were wandering elsewhere.

He became very adept at this and was soon passed from the awkward squad to the Company. By this time he was no longer seized with an uncontrollable desire to burst into laughter whenever he saw a platoon or section "Present Arms," and all smack the sides of their rifles at the same moment. Instead, it became a matter of pride to him that his own smack was never half-a-second too early or too late. He was, in fact, no longer plain Amadu Frafra but Private Amadu Frafra, of the Gold Coast Regiment.

The white sergeant kept a friendly eye on Amadu, and had no reason to regret his judgment. Amadu showed himself good military material—smart, intelligent, eager to obey orders. Therefore, in the course of time, when another Bren-gun crew was being formed, Private Amadu Frafra was selected; and selected not to be a mere ammunition number but the No. 1 himself, with the duty of firing the gun. His pride in his new status became overweening. The Bren-gun itself might have been a personal gift bestowed on him by the British King. Whenever he considered his gun numbers were encroaching on his prerogatives he brushed them aside with the remark:

"You no savvy proper like me. I fit to be Number One Bren gunner."

Later on there was Bren gun practice on the range just

the other side of the golf course. Amadu learned to 'typewrite.'

Tat . . . tat tat . . . tat tat tat. . . . And then followed bursts of fire, ten rounds at a time, or so. Which was what Amadu enjoyed most.

The white sergeant watched Amadu's progress with a friendly but critical eye.

"Now listen to me," he said at last. "I see what your trouble is. You're in too much of a hurry to press that trigger. You've got to learn to take your time. Wait till the enemy's well in range. Savvy?"

Whereupon Amadu rolled his eyes and grinned in assent whether he understood it all or not.

Then came the War, and Private Amadu Frafra and his fellows learned they were going to fight Hitler's friend, Mussolini the Italian, in Abyssinia. They would have preferred it to be Hitler direct, because most of them knew he had referred to them in a book as 'niggers'—and they strongly objected to the term. 'Negroes' they thought bad enough. Generically, they preferred to be called Africans. Or if that seemed a bit too presumptuous, they would be content with 'West Africans.'

The white sergeant, passing Amadu on the barrack square one morning stopped and said in pidgin English:

"How you like going in big fight, Amadu?"

The superb white teeth flashed in the sunshine.

"Me no fear," was the reply. "If my time catch, ah, well, it be god palaver."

"That's the idea," said the sergeant, patting him approvingly on the shoulder, as he passed on.

Soon the Regiment went down to Accra and travelled by train along the coast to the port of Takoradi. Here a big liner was ready to take them to the other side of Africa.

Most of them had never seen such a ship before. Amadu was one of them. But he had to uphold his reputation as No. 1 Bren-gunner with much 'savvy.' While the other natives stared and wondered Amadu briefly explained the whole matter.

"This ship, he all same like motor-car," he said. "He fit to go front; he fit to go back."

On the voyage out the Bren-gunners resumed their interrupted training. One morning they squatted on the deck round a blackboard on which the white sergeant was drawing with a bit of chalk. When he had finished he stood aside and revealed a strange hooded-looking monster.

"Never seen anything like that before, have you?" he said. "Well, there's lots of things in this war you haven't seen—not as yet. That's what we call an armoured car. You'll be running up against them most likely. But you've no need to be scared. They can't hurt you. Not-if-you-do-exactly-what-I'm-going-to-tell-you," with much emphasis.

Then the sergeant with the aid of more diagrams on the blackboard explained patiently and minutely the most vulnerable parts of an armoured car. He tried to drill into their heads the importance of aiming at particular spots—where the driver sat, the radiator, the tyres, if the car was coming straight at them. If they had a side target then they were to go for the engine underneath the armouring, which meant lying very flat down on the ground. But most of all he harped on the necessity for holding their fire till the very last moment.

"Don't go blazing away as soon as they come into sight," he insisted. "Wait till they are within forty yards. And thirty yards is better still. And twenty's better than that. Then give it to 'em proper, just where I've told you to. And you'll see something that'll make you laugh. Remember, hold your fire to the last moment. It's just as simple as that. The motto is, as we say, 'Don't shoot till you see the whites of their eyes.' Get that into your heads and it's easy."

So that there should be no doubt about the gunners getting this into their heads, the native sergeant standing by translated it into the men's own language. Which took a little time as some of the white sergeant's idioms had to be approached in a roundabout way.

"Told 'em?" asked the white sergeant when the other ceased speaking.

The native sergeant nodded.

"Then start and tell *him* all over again," said the white

sergeant, pointing specially to Private Amadu Frafra. " He's the one I'm most concerned about."

So it was recited all over again for the benefit of Amadu, who took this as a mark of special distinction and grinned with pride.

" Savvy ? " inquired the white sergeant, at length.

And Amadu assured him that he did by pointing to the whites of his own eyes, at the same time rolling them so much that they looked as large as the whites of poached eggs.

Some of the regiment's Bren guns were mounted on the top deck as ack-ack guns, and Amadu did watches with the other gunners. His own gun was locked up in the ship's armoury but he got it out as often as he could. He spent hours of his spare time oiling and polishing it while the other soldiers squatted about on the deck and played cowrie shells for cigarettes.

Round the Cape the troopship ran into very dirty weather, and Amadu learned for the first time, like the rest of them, that sea-sickness makes death seem easy, and that it is no respecter of persons. 'No. 1 Bren-gunner' suffered among the worst. He no longer haunted the ship's armoury.

" My belly, he be sick proper," he gasped to the over-worked M.O. " Everything he go round and round."

And for the hundredth time the M.O. tried to restore confidence by a simplified explanation of the action of a rough sea upon the solar plexus. But what did them more good was when, in the intervals of their own miseries, they hung over the side of the vessel and watched the other ships in the convoy being tossed about at most alarming angles. They howled with delight at the sight.

After trying in vain for three days to make Capetown the troopship continued round to Simonstown, and thence to Durban where the regiment was to disembark and board another vessel that was to take them up to Mombasa. The white officers and N.C.O.'s were a little anxious about what might happen at Durban. They had heard a lot about colour prejudice in the Union. But they were agreeably surprised. As the regiment marched singing through the town, cheering crowds lined the streets and loaded the West African troops with gifts of fruit and cigarettes. Amadu stepped out proudly near the head of the column, his Bren gun slung across his back in its leather sling. And when the white women offered him cigarettes or fruit he grinned like a big happy child and said :

" He fit to fight for British people all the time."

By now Amadu and his Bren gun were inseparable. After disembarking at Mombasa the regiment travelled north in goods trucks to Namjahi, whence they made a forced march of five hundred miles to Isiola. This was a painful experience because they were now in mountainous country. The rarefied air at eight thousand feet affected the lungs of men used only to breathing a sea-level atmosphere. Amadu suffered with the others. One day the white sergeant, seeing him staggering along breathless with his Bren gun slung behind him, shouted to the loader to give Amadu some relief, by carrying the gun for a spell. But Amadu flatly refused to hand it over, though it had grown to weigh a ton.

" This thing be mine. No one else fit touch um," was his final word on the matter.

At last they reached Wajir, up near the frontier in the north-east of Kenya, which was to be the springboard for their advance into Italian Somaliland. And it was at Wajir that Amadu assured himself beyond all doubt that destiny had big things in store for him. On the night of his arrival he saw, low in the heavens, the 'star with a tail on.'

" This thing be proper juju," he informed the white sergeant in his excitement. " Him tail, he point for Italian, and when we meet um we fit beat um proper."

" You're telling me ! " laughed the sergeant.

* * *

The attack on the Italians had begun, and a battalion of the Gold Coast Regiment was making a compass march during the night in order to surprise the left flank of the enemy at Allessandra. They reached their positions just before daybreak, and splitting up into small sections, began to move forward cautiously on a front of about a couple of miles. The country was flat though rough, dotted here and there with clumps of bushes and small trees, and covered with tallish dry grass in which a handful of men with a machine gun could easily lie unseen until trodden-on.

It was also easy for the individual sections to lose sight of one another as they wormed their way through the thick close tufts of grass that covered the plain; and the runners sent out by the company officers with orders had first-rate opportunities of exhibiting their skill as bushmen.

Thus it happened that about eight o'clock in the morning, with the sun already blazing down fiercely from a cloudless sky, Private Amadu Frafra, popping his head up over the top of the long grass, could see no trace of the rest of his company, either to the right of him, or to the left, or in front. He and his Bren-gun crew seemed completely isolated. They had crawled up to the position indicated by the platoon officer when the advance first began and since then nothing had happened. They had seen nobody, and heard not a sound but the buzzing of the swarms of big flies. In front of Amadu the Bren-gun, mounted on its small tripod and with the magazine on in readiness, stood almost concealed in the grass. Another magazine lay alongside, with the loader sprawled out near it. The tripod carrier and the ammunition number crouched patiently in the rear. They were having a very dull time. Amadu had ordered them not to raise their heads on any account.

Another half-hour passed and still no further orders had reached Amadu. But this did not worry him. He had been told to stay there; and he had a plentiful supply of kola nuts to chew. And still chewing, he once more lifted his head above the grass to reconnoitre. Instantly his jaws stopped and his big eyes bulged.

"What this thing that come?" he shouted.

His three companions glad to be allowed to look at something at last, immediately thrust their heads up and stared across the rough plain in front of them. They saw what Amadu had seen, but they had no reply to make to his question. Moving in their direction, just over a mile away, were five strange-looking objects spread out in a rough line, and about a quarter of a mile from each other. Four of them were away to the right of the gun position. But the fifth seemed to be travelling straight towards it. They were dark grey vehicles, narrow-looking and tallish by reason of their turrets. And their shuttered armouring had a decidedly sinister appearance in the eyes of the Bren-gun crew, none of whom had as yet seen an armoured car. They gazed with open mouths in silence at these threatening apparitions, especially the one which was making a bee-line for them.

Amadu was the first to speak.

" I tink it be Italian armoured car like baturi (master) tell us," he said. " I tink I fit kill this one."

Four of the cars were by now steering a course well away to his right. But the fifth continued to make its way steadily towards them. It came along slowly, bumping over the rough ground at not much more than walking-pace. Amadu lay stretched out behind his gun, holding it tightly, and never taking his eye from the sight for a moment. Suddenly there came a short burst of machine-gun fire from the armoured car. It was not directed at them in particular. Evidently the occupants of the car were a bit nervous and were occasionally spraying the ground in front in case anyone was about. A few bullets whipped through the grass near the crouching Bren-gun crew.

" I no like this one," observed the ammunition carrier uneasily, taking another quick peep at the oncoming monster.

" Make you all go back small, and lef me," ordered Amadu, peremptorily, meaning that they were all to get under cover and that he would manage the affair on his own.

His three companions gladly availed themselves of the privilege of taking cover in a small copse some thirty yards to the rear. They by no means shared Amadu's confidence in his ability to ' kill this one.'

Left alone, Amadu concentrated all his attention on the advancing car. It was still bouncing along straight for him, and when about three hundred yards away another burst of fire came from its turret. Most of the bullets whistled over his head and he could hear them clipping the twigs of the bushes behind him. His finger automatically curled round the trigger.

But just as he was about to press on it he recalled the white sergeant's instructions. Baturi had said he was to hold his fire till the armoured car came very close. He was not to shoot till he saw the whites of its eyes. Then, baturi had said, he would see something that would make him laugh. So Amadu curbed his impatience, and lay silent and hidden in the grass while the armoured car drew nearer and nearer. Even the bullet that whipped off his hat and allowed the flies to settle on the sweating shaven parts of his scalp that the scorpion left uncovered, failed to rouse him to retaliation.

The armoured car steadily approached. It was only a hundred yards away. Amadu thought it now looked much bigger and more threatening. But, with his eye along the sight of the gun and his finger on the trigger he hadn't the slightest fear. Had not the white sergeant assured him on the ship that the armoured car couldn't hurt him if he did what he was told? And Amadu believed him implicitly. He'd be quite safe if he waited till he saw the whites of its eyes.

There were four round holes in a line across the front of the car, just below the turret. As it came slowly nearer and nearer Amadu could see them quite plainly. These, he made up his mind, must be the eyes the sergeant attributed so much importance to. But so far there was no sign of any white in them. Staring fixedly at them along his gun Amadu could see nothing except four black sockets. Away over to his right he could hear quite a lot of machine-gun fire in the direction taken by the other armoured cars. The sound sorely tempted him to start firing himself, but with the white sergeant's exhortation firmly fixed in his mind he continued to lie silent and motionless in the grass.

Still the grey, shrouded monster persisted in its juggernaut-like progress towards him. Forty yards away . . . thirty . . . twenty. . . .

Amadu remembered that the sergeant had told him that twenty yards was all right. At the same time, he hadn't seen any sign of the whites of the eyes yet. And it was upon this that the sergeant had laid greatest stress.

The twenty yards was reduced to fifteen. For the moment the car's machine-guns had ceased firing. In any case, Amadu would have been safe from them now even if he had been spotted. They could not have been depressed sufficiently, so close was the car to him.

Amadu did not know this at the time. He did not even think about it. But he did begin to grow very puzzled because, although the monster was almost on top of him, still he hadn't caught so much as a glimpse of the whites of any of the four eyes.

Under cover in the copse behind crouched the other three members of the gun team also watching, with eyes starting from their heads, the relentless progress of the armoured car. They were too spellbound to move. They just waited, staring, for the car to roll over Amadu and his Bren-gun and flatten him out.

Twelve yards. . . .

And now, just when his faith in the white sergeant was beginning to waver, Amadu saw what he had been waiting for.

Inside one of the four dark holes below the turret of the car something white showed. Probably it was a glint of the sun reflected from the driver's glass pane behind the armouring, or from some piece of polished metal. But for Amadu it was the promised white of the eye. He waited no longer. With cheek tight against the side of his gun butt he took careful aim and pressed the trigger. A stream of bullets tore through the armour on the front of the car.

To his surprise, however, there did not follow the 'something to make him laugh' which the white sergeant had promised would happen in due course if his instructions were faithfully carried out. Instead, much to Amadu's dismay, the monster continued unchecked its lumbering career straight for him. He had just time to roll over and over on his side, dragging his gun with him, before it crashed over the very spot where he had been lying. He managed to save himself, but a leg of the Bren-gun tripod was smashed under a wheel of the car.

As soon as he recovered himself Amadu jumped to his feet, heedless of danger, and ran towards the armoured car which had now come to a standstill against a tree a few yards away. His one thought was to exact vengeance for the injury done to his gun. But as he drew near, the door in the side of the car opened and two very scared-looking Italians wearing berets and olive-green uniforms, clambered out with their hands raised. When they saw Amadu, with the Bren-gun pointing their way, they began shouting frenziedly to him in language he could not understand. But he understood well enough that they were surrendering.

By now he had been joined by the rest of his gun team. They all walked up and gazed inside the car. The driver had fallen forward in his seat. He was dead. He had caught the full force of Amadu's volley in his chest. Leaning heavily against the driver was another man in a beret, also dead. And on the floor in the rear of the car lay a third Italian, badly wounded and groaning in pain. A faint odour of cordite filled the interior, and here and there little curls of smoke began to appear, and a smell of burning. Amadu, still covering his prisoners with his Bren-gun, ordered his companions to drag the three bodies out of the car and to put out the flames that were spreading.

It was while they were so engaged that the Platoon Officer appeared. He had been making his way over to the Bren-gun post, and had witnessed all the closing stages of the little drama. He seized Amadu by the hand and shook it vigorously.

"That was the finest bit of work I've ever seen," he said, with enthusiasm.

Amadu's teeth flashed in a wide grin, and he rolled the whites of his big eyes with pleasure at the praise.

"This thing be easy," he replied. "I fit do some more."

And then, remembering that it was some time since he had had a meal, he added as an afterthought:

"But my belly hunger too much."

The Platoon Officer, thinking of Battalion H.Q. only three hundred yards behind, right in the track of that armoured car, and visualising it in process of being shot up laughed loudly.

"I can promise you a belly-full such as you've never dreamed of, my lad, when the Colonel hears about this," he said.

THE END